BRAVE NEW
WORLD

ALSO BY

FRED FORDHAM

To Kill A Mockingbird: A Graphic Novel

The Adventures of John Blake

BRAVE NEW WORLD

A GRAPHIC NOVEL

ADAPTED AND ILLUSTRATED BY

FRED FORDHAM

1 3 5 7 9 10 8 6 4 2

Vintage Classics is part of the Penguin Random House group of companies whose
addresses can be found at global.penguinrandomhouse.com

Original text copyright © 1932, 1946 Aldous Huxley
Illustrations and adaption of text copyright © 2022 Fred Fordham

Aldous Huxley and Fred Fordham have asserted their right to be identified as the authors of
this Work in accordance with the Copyright, Designs and Patents Act 1988

First published in Great Britain by Vintage Classics in 2022

penguin.co.uk/vintage-classics

A CIP catalogue record for this book is available from the British Library

ISBN 9781784877736

Printed and bound in Latvia by Livonia Print SIA

The authorised representative in the EEA is Penguin Random House Ireland, Morrison
Chambers, 32 Nassau Street, Dublin D02 YH68

Penguin Random House is committed to a sustainable future for our business, our readers
and our planet. This book is made from Forest Stewardship Council® certified paper.

ACKNOWLEDGMENTS

Special thanks to Mary Gaule and Jennifer Civiletto for overseeing this project and keeping all the plates spinning; to Camille Johnston and Ros Asquith for their essential editorial feedback; to my agent, Jenny Savill, for her constant support; and to the Huxley Estate for involving me in bringing this strange and insightful piece of philosophy/fiction to a new medium.

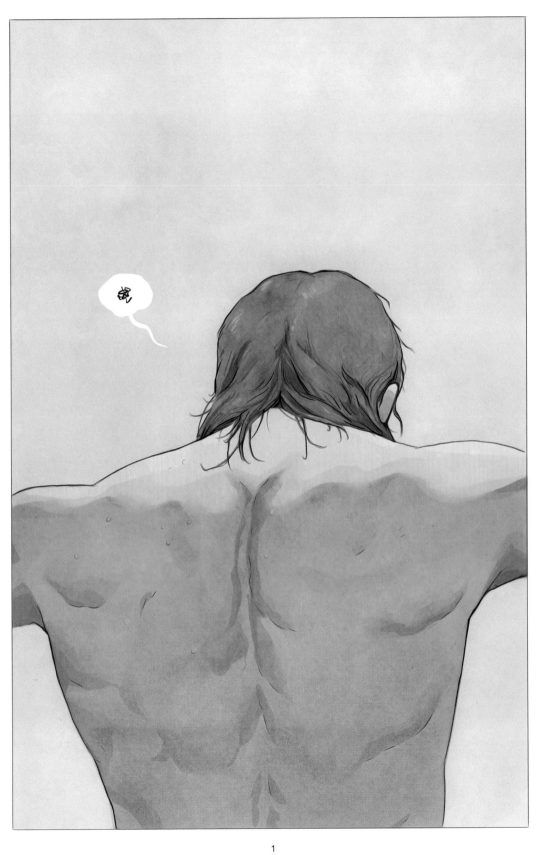

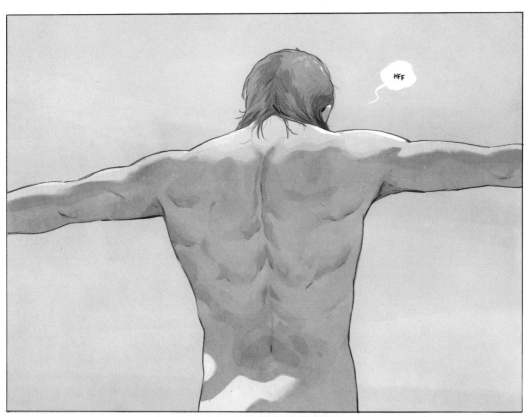

3

HWUH

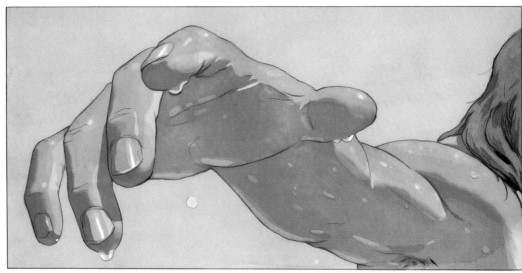

4

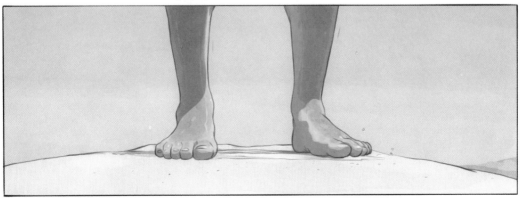

FOR A GENERAL IDEA YOU MUST HAVE IF YOU ARE TO DO YOUR WORK INTELLIGENTLY.

ALBEIT AS LITTLE OF ONE AS POSSIBLE, IF YOU ARE TO BE GOOD AND HAPPY MEMBERS OF SOCIETY. PARTICULARS, NOT GENERALITIES, MAKE FOR VIRTUE AND HAPPINESS.

BOOP

NOT PHILOSOPHERS BUT FRET-SAWYERS AND STAMP COLLECTORS COMPOSE THE BACKBONE OF SOCIETY.

AND THIS IS THE FERTILIZING ROOM.

HAPPY

TOMORROW YOU'LL BE SETTLING DOWN TO SERIOUS WORK. YOU WON'T HAVE TIME FOR GENERALITIES.

MEANWHILE, I SHALL BEGIN AT THE BEGINNING.

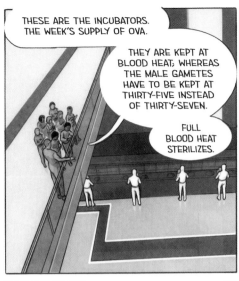

THESE ARE THE INCUBATORS. THE WEEK'S SUPPLY OF OVA.

THEY ARE KEPT AT BLOOD HEAT; WHEREAS THE MALE GAMETES HAVE TO BE KEPT AT THIRTY-FIVE INSTEAD OF THIRTY-SEVEN.

FULL BLOOD HEAT STERILIZES.

RAMS WRAPPED IN THERMOGENE BEGET NO LAMBS.

GAMETES
- Males at blood heat—?
- Rams wrapped i
beget no lan

THE MODERN FERTILIZING PROCESS BEGINS, OF COURSE, WITH A SURGICAL PROCEDURE. THIS IS UNDERGONE VOLUNTARILY FOR THE GOOD OF SOCIETY, NOT TO MENTION THE FACT THAT IT CARRIES A BONUS AMOUNTING TO SIX MONTHS' SALARY.

ONCE COUNTED AND INSPECTED FOR ABNORMALITIES, THE OVA ARE THEN IMMERSED IN A WARM BOUILLON CONTAINING FREE-SWIMMING SPERMATOZOA.

THE FERTILIZED OVA ARE THEN RETURNED TO THE INCUBATORS.

ALPHAS AND BETAS REMAIN UNTIL DEFINITELY BOTTLED, WHILE GAMMAS, DELTAS, AND EPSILONS ARE REMOVED AGAIN AFTER THIRTY-SIX HOURS TO UNDERGO BOKANOVSKY'S PROCESS.

THIS BEING THE MASS PRODUCTION OF IDENTICAL TWINS, AND ONE OF THE MAJOR INSTRUMENTS OF SOCIAL STABILITY.

- fertilized ova → incubators.
- Gammas, deltas and epsilons → Bok process.
Bok process
- Major instrum

STANDARDIZED MEN AND WOMEN IN UNIFORM BATCHES. AN ENTIRE FACTORY STAFFED WITH THE PRODUCTS OF A SINGLE BOKANOVSKIFIED EGG.

THE PRINCIPLE OF THE ASSEMBLY LINE AT LAST APPLIED TO BIOLOGY.

PROGRESS.

MR. FOSTER, CAN YOU TELL US THE RECORD NUMBER OF INDIVIDUALS FOR A SINGLE OVARY?

SIXTEEN THOUSAND AND TWELVE IN THIS CENTER.

IN ONE HUNDRED AND EIGHTY-NINE BATCHES OF IDENTICALS.

THEY'VE DONE MUCH BETTER IN SOME OVERSEAS CENTERS. STILL, WE MEAN TO BEAT THEM IF WE CAN.

THAT'S THE SPIRIT I LIKE!

SCRIT SCRIT

COME ALONG WITH US, MR. FOSTER, AND GIVE THESE STUDENTS THE BENEFIT OF YOUR EXPERT KNOWLEDGE.

WITH PLEASURE.

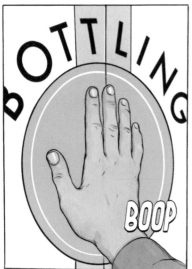

BOTTLING

BOOP

THE SOCIAL PREDESTINATORS SEND THEIR FIGURES TO THE FERTILIZERS.

WHO GIVE THEM THE EMBRYOS THEY ASK FOR.

AND THE BOTTLES COME IN HERE TO BE PREDESTINED IN DETAIL.

AFTER WHICH THEY ARE SENT DOWN TO THE EMBRYO STORE.

WHERE WE NOW PROCEED OURSELVES.

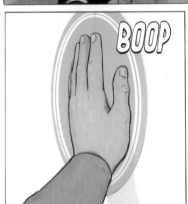

BOOP

EMBRYOS ARE LIKE PHOTOGRAPH FILM. THEY CAN ONLY STAND RED LIGHT.

2 EMBRYO STO

BING

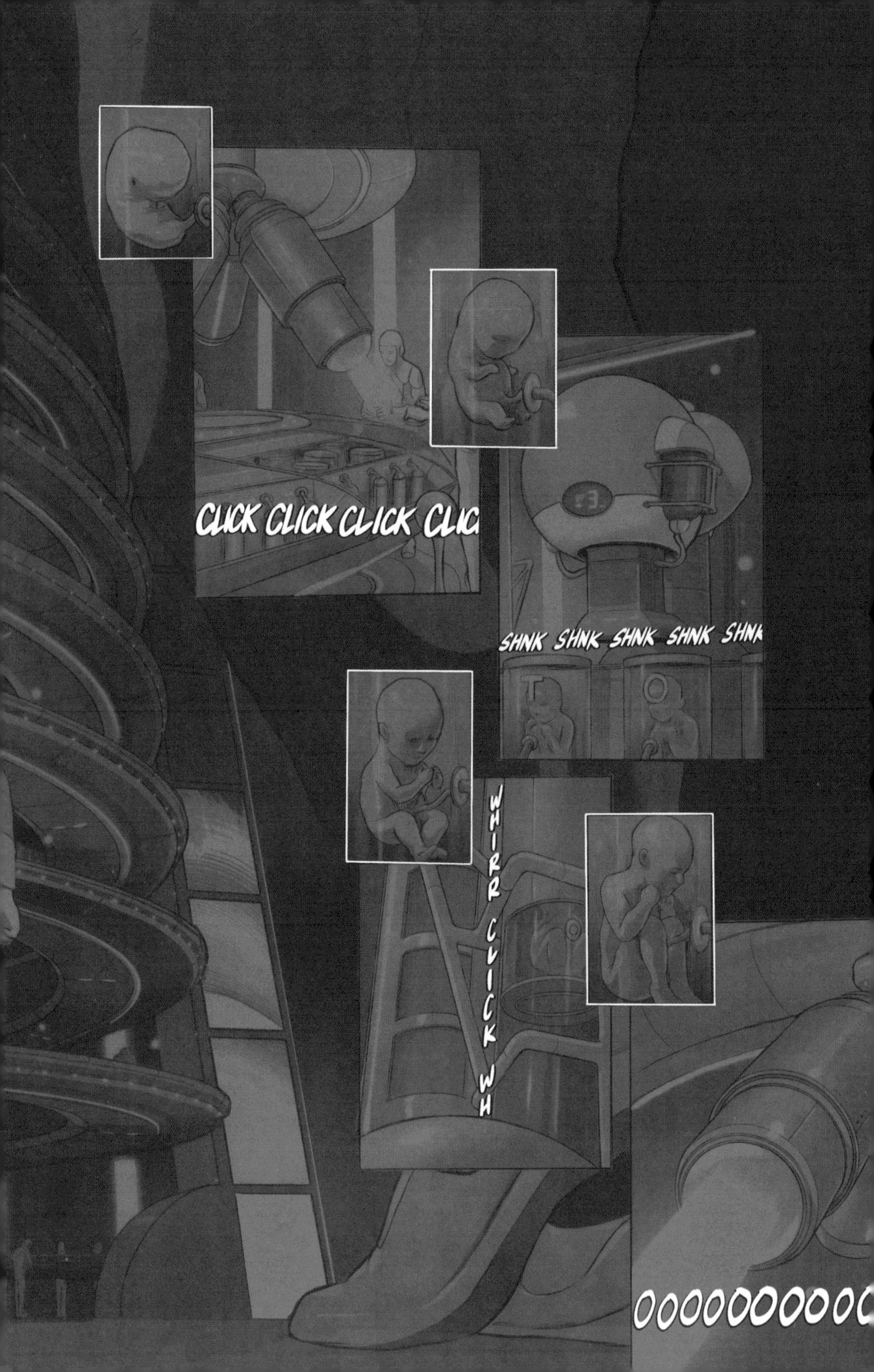

CLICK CLICK CLICK CLICK

SHNK SHNK SHNK SHNK SHNK

WHIRR CLICK WH

OOOOOOOOOO

THERE YOU CAN SEE THE RESERVOIR OF BLOOD SURROGATE ON WHICH OUR EMBRYOS FEED.

"T" FOR MALE, CIRCLE FOR FEMALE, OF COURSE. WHO CAN TELL ME WHAT THE QUESTION MARK SIGNIFIES?

FREEMARTINS, SIR.

QUITE SO. FOR OF COURSE IN THE VAST MAJORITY OF CASES, FERTILITY IS MERELY A NUISANCE. THOSE DECANTED AS FREEMARTINS ARE STRUCTURALLY QUITE NORMAL, BUT STERILE.

AND WE DO NOT CONTENT OURSELVES WITH MERELY HATCHING OUT EMBRYOS. ANY COW CAN DO THAT. WE ALSO PREDESTINE AND CONDITION. WE DECANT OUR BABIES AS SOCIALIZED HUMAN BEINGS, AS ALPHAS OR EPSILONS, AS FUTURE SEWAGE WORKERS OR FUTURE DIRECTORS OF HATCHERIES.

DOWN HERE WE CONDITION THEM TO THRIVE ON THAT FOR WHICH THEY ARE PREDESTINED.

AND OUR COLLEAGUES UPSTAIRS TEACH THEM TO LOVE IT.

AND THAT IS THE SECRET OF HAPPINESS AND VIRTUE--LIKING WHAT YOU'VE *GOT* TO DO.

TEN TO THREE.

WE MUST GO UP TO THE HYPNOPAEDIA NURSERIES BEFORE THE CHILDREN HAVE FINISHED THEIR AFTERNOON SLEEP . . .

THANK YOU FOR YOUR TIME, MR. FOSTER.

INFANT NURSERIES
CONDITIONING

NEO-PAVLOVIAN

BOOP

WATCH
CAREFULLY.

OBSERVE.

OBSERVE.

16

AND NOW WE PROCEED TO RUB IN THE LESSON WITH A MILD ELECTRIC SHOCK.

WE CAN ELECTRIFY THAT WHOLE STRIP OF FLOOR.

THEY'LL GROW UP WITH AN INSTINCTIVE HATRED OF BOOKS AND FLOWERS. A LOATHING OF INTELLECTUAL PURSUITS AND OF NATURE. PERFECT FOR FACTORY WORK, YOU SEE? PERFECT DELTAS.

COME.

ONCE UPON A TIME, WHILE OUR FORD WAS STILL ON EARTH, THERE WAS A LITTLE BOY CALLED REUBEN RABINOVITCH. REUBEN WAS THE CHILD OF POLISH-SPEAKING PARENTS.

YOU KNOW WHAT POLISH IS, I SUPPOSE?

A DEAD LANGUAGE.

LIKE FRENCH OR GERMAN.

AND "PARENT"?

WELL? IT IS SCIENCE, AFTER ALL, NOT SMUT.

H-HUMAN BEINGS USED TO BE . . .

WELL, THEY USED TO BE VIVIPAROUS.

QUITE RIGHT.

AND WHEN THEY WERE DECANTED . . .

"BORN."

WELL, THEN THEY WERE THE PARENTS-- I MEAN, NOT THE BABIES, OF COURSE; THE OTHER ONES . . .

IN SHORT, THE PARENTS WERE THE FATHER AND THE MOTHER.

MOTHER.

HYPNO PAEDIA

BOOP

THESE ARE UNPLEASANT FACTS; I KNOW. BUT THEN, MOST HISTORICAL FACTS ARE UNPLEASANT.

21

THE EARLY EXPERIMENTERS THOUGHT THAT HYPNOPAEDIA COULD BE MADE AN INSTRUMENT OF INTELLECTUAL EDUCATION . . .

WHEREAS IF THEY'D ONLY STARTED WITH *MORAL* EDUCATION.

MORAL EDUCATION, WHICH OUGHT NEVER, IN ANY CIRCUMSTANCES, TO BE RATIONAL.

WHAT'S THE LESSON THIS AFTERNOON?

WE HAD ELEMENTARY SEX FOR THE FIRST FORTY MINUTES, BUT NOW IT'S SWITCHED TO ELEMENTARY CLASS CONSCIOUSNESS.

...ALL WEAR GREEN, AND DELTA CHILDREN ALL WEAR KHAKI...

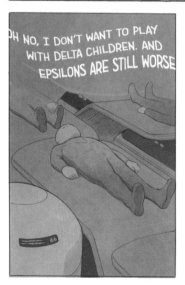

OH NO, I DON'T WANT TO PLAY WITH DELTA CHILDREN. AND EPSILONS ARE STILL WORSE

THEY'RE TOO STUPID TO BE ABLE TO READ OR WRITE.

BESIDES, THEY WEAR BLACK, WHICH IS SUCH A BEASTLY COLOR . .

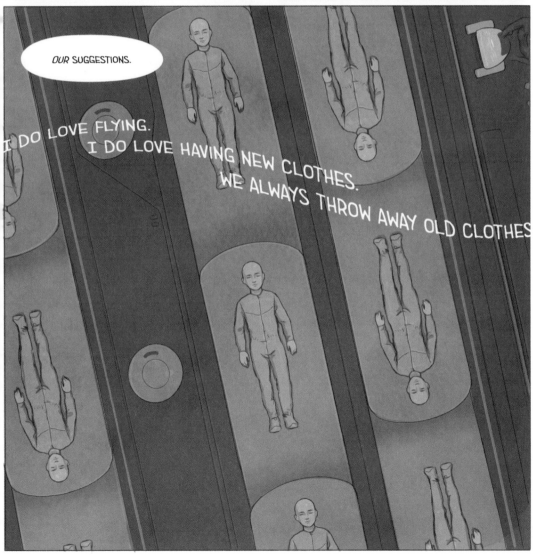

MAIN DAY-SHIFT OFF DUTY. SECOND DAY-SHIFT TAKE OVER. MAIN DAY-SHIFT OFF . . .

. . . DUTY. SECOND DAY-SHIFT TAKE OVER. MAIN DAY-SHIFT OFF DUTY. SECOND DAY-SHIFT TAKE OVER . . .

BETA CHANGING ROOMS

BERNARD MARX
ALPHA PLUS
PSYCHOLOGY dept.

Have a gre
Evening, Bern

BERNARD MARX
ALPHA PLUS
PSY [HOLOGY dept.

MEN'S CHANGING ROOMS

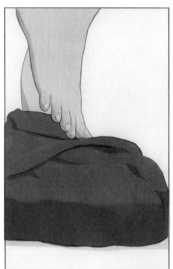

STRANGE TO THINK THAT EVEN IN OUR FORD'S DAY MOST GAMES WERE PLAYED WITHOUT MORE APPARATUS THAN A BALL OR TWO AND A FEW STICKS AND PERHAPS A BIT OF NETTING.

IMAGINE THE FOLLY OF ALLOWING PEOPLE TO PLAY COMPLEX GAMES WHICH DO NOTHING WHATEVER TO INCREASE CONSUMPTION. IT'S MADNESS.

NOWADAYS THE CONTROLLERS WON'T APPROVE OF ANY NEW GAME UNLESS IT CAN BE SHOWN THAT IT REQUIRES AT LEAST AS MUCH APPARATUS AS THE MOST COMPLICATED EXISTING GAMES.

-AAAAAH

WHAT'S THE MATTER?

NOTHING MUCH. IT'S JUST THAT THIS LITTLE BOY SEEMS RATHER RELUCTANT TO JOIN IN THE ORDINARY EROTIC PLAY.

-SNF-

I DIDN'T MEAN TO HURT HIM OR ANYTHING. HONESTLY.

OF COURSE YOU DIDN'T, DEAR.

AND SO, I'M TAKING HIM IN TO SEE THE ASSISTANT SUPERINTENDENT OF PSYCHOLOGY. JUST TO SEE IF ANYTHING'S AT ALL ABNORMAL.

QUITE RIGHT. TAKE HIM IN.

WHAT I'M GOING TO TELL YOU NOW MAY SOUND INCREDIBLE.

BUT FOR A VERY LONG PERIOD BEFORE OUR FORD, AND EVEN FOR SOME GENERATIONS AFTERWARD, EROTIC PLAY BETWEEN CHILDREN HAD BEEN REGARDED AS ABNORMAL.

NO!

NOT ONLY ABNORMAL BUT IMMORAL.

BUT . . . WHAT HAPPENED? WHAT WERE THE RESULTS?

THE RESULTS . . .

. . . WERE TERRIBLE.

HULLO, FANNY. WHO ARE YOU GOING OUT WITH TONIGHT?

OH, HULLO, LENINA.

NOBODY.

NOBODY?

I'VE BEEN FEELING RATHER OUT OF SORTS LATELY. DR. WELLS ADVISED ME TO HAVE A PREGNANCY SUBSTITUTE.

HE SAYS THAT A THREE MONTHS' PREGNANCY SUBSTITUTE NOW WILL MAKE ALL THE DIFFERENCE TO MY HEALTH FOR THE NEXT THREE OR FOUR YEARS.

WELL, I HOPE HE'S RIGHT. BUT DO YOU REALLY MEAN TO SAY THAT FOR THE NEXT THREE MONTHS YOU'RE NOT SUPPOSED TO . . .

OH NO, DEAR. ONLY FOR A WEEK OR TWO, THAT'S ALL. I SUPPOSE YOU'RE GOING OUT?

MM-HMM.

WHO WITH?

HENRY FOSTER.

AGAIN?

YOU MEAN TO TELL ME YOU'RE *STILL* GOING OUT WITH HENRY FOSTER?

IT'S ONLY ABOUT FOUR MONTHS I'VE BEEN HAVING HENRY.

TERRIBLE.

CONTROLLER! WHAT AN UNEXPECTED PLEASURE!

CHILDREN, WHAT ARE YOU THINKING OF? THIS IS THE RESIDENT CONTROLLER FOR WESTERN EUROPE, HIS FORDSHIP MUSTAPHA MOND.

YOU ALL REMEMBER, I SUPPOSE, THAT BEAUTIFUL AND INSPIRED SAYING OF OUR FORD'S: HISTORY IS BUNK.

HISTORY.

IS BUNK.

ONLY FOUR MONTHS! I LIKE THAT. AND THERE'S BEEN NOBODY ELSE EXCEPT HENRY ALL THAT TIME. HAS THERE?

NO, THERE HASN'T BEEN ANYONE ELSE.

I REALLY DO THINK YOU OUGHT TO BE CAREFUL. IT'S SUCH HORRIBLY BAD FORM TO GO ON AND ON LIKE THIS WITH ONE MAN.

THAT'S WHY YOU'RE TAUGHT NO HISTORY. BUT NOW THE TIME HAS COME . . .

IT'S ALL RIGHT, DIRECTOR. I WON'T CORRUPT THEM.

YOU KNOW HOW STRONGLY THE DIRECTOR OBJECTS TO ANYTHING INTENSE OR LONG-DRAWN. FOUR MONTHS OF HENRY FOSTER WITHOUT HAVING ANOTHER MAN--WHY, HE'D BE FURIOUS IF HE KNEW.

JUST TRY TO REALIZE IT. TRY TO REALIZE WHAT IT WAS LIKE TO HAVE A VIVIPAROUS MOTHER.

THERE'S NO NEED TO GIVE HIM UP. HAVE SOMEBODY ELSE FROM TIME TO TIME, THAT'S ALL. HE HAS OTHER GIRLS DOESN'T HE?

OF COURSE.

TRY TO IMAGINE WHAT "LIVING WITH ONE'S FAMILY" MEANT.

OF COURSE HE DOES. TRUST HENRY FOSTER TO BE THE PERFECT GENTLEMAN-- ALWAYS CORRECT.

HOME--A FEW SMALL ROOMS, STIFLINGLY OVER-INHABITED BY A MAN, BY A PERIODICALLY TEEMING WOMAN, BY A RABBLE OF BOYS AND GIRLS OF ALL AGES.

YOU OUGHT TO BE A LITTLE MORE PROMISCUOUS.

SOMEHOW I HAVEN'T BEEN FEELING VERY KEEN ON PROMISCUITY LATELY.

NO AIR, NO SPACE; AN UNDERSTERILIZED PRISON; DARKNESS, DISEASE, AND *SMELLS.*

BUT ONE'S GOT TO MAKE THE EFFORT, LENINA. AFTER ALL, EVERYONE BELONGS TO EVERYONE ELSE.

YES, EVERYONE BELONGS TO EVERYONE ELSE.

AND PSYCHICALLY, THE HOME WAS A RABBIT HOLE, A MIDDEN, HOT WITH THE FRICTIONS OF TIGHTLY PACKED LIFE, REEKING WITH EMOTION.

WHAT SUFFOCATING INTIMACIES, WHAT DANGEROUS, INSANE, OBSCENE RELATIONSHIPS BETWEEN MEMBERS OF THE FAMILY GROUP!

YOU'RE QUITE RIGHT, FANNY. AS USUAL. I'LL MAKE THE EFFORT.

MANIACALLY THE MOTHER BROODED OVER HER CHILDREN--*HER* CHILDREN--LIKE A CAT OVER ITS KITTENS; BUT A CAT THAT COULD TALK, A CAT THAT COULD SAY, "MY BABY, MY BABY, AND OH, OH, AT MY BREAST, THE LITTLE HANDS, THE HUNGER, AND THAT UNSPEAKABLE AGONIZING PLEASURE!"

YES, YOU MAY WELL SHUDDER.

TO TELL THE TRUTH, I'M BEGINNING TO GET JUST A TINY BIT BORED WITH NOTHING BUT HENRY EVERY DAY.

DO YOU KNOW BERNARD MARX?

GOING TO THE FEELIES TONIGHT, HENRY?

I HEAR THE NEW ONE AT THE ALHAMBRA IS FIRST-RATE.

THERE'S A LOVE SCENE ON A BEARSKIN RUG; THEY SAY IT'S MARVELLOUS. THE MOST AMAZING TACTUAL EFFECTS.

I'LL MAKE A POINT OF GOING.

OUR FORD--OR OUR FREUD, AS, FOR SOME INSCRUTABLE REASON, HE CHOSE TO CALL HIMSELF WHENEVER HE SPOKE OF PSYCHOLOGICAL MATTERS--HAD BEEN THE FIRST TO REVEAL THE APPALLING DANGERS OF FAMILY LIFE.

LENINA, YOU DON'T MEAN TO SAY . . .?

WHY NOT? BERNARD'S AN ALPHA-PLUS.

LENINA CROWNE?

OH, SHE'S A SPLENDID GIRL. WONDERFULLY PNEUMATIC. I'M SURPRISED YOU HAVEN'T HAD HER.

MOTHERS AND FATHERS, BROTHERS AND SISTERS. BUT THERE WERE ALSO HUSBANDS, WIVES, LOVERS. THERE WERE ALSO MONOGAMY AND ROMANCE.

I CAN'T THINK HOW IT IS I HAVEN'T. I CERTAINLY WILL. AT THE FIRST OPPORTUNITY.

YES, I REALLY DO ADVISE YOU TO TRY HER.

EVERYONE BELONGS TO EVERYONE ELSE.

HE ASKED ME TO GO TO ONE OF THE SAVAGE RESERVATIONS WITH HIM. I'VE ALWAYS WANTED TO GO TO A SAVAGE RESERVATION.

BUT HIS REPUTATION? THEY SAY HE SPENDS MOST OF HIS TIME BY HIMSELF--ALONE.

EVERYWHERE EXCLUSIVENESS. MOTHER! MY LOVE! MY BABY! NO WONDER THOSE POOR PRE-MODERNS WERE MAD AND WICKED AND MISERABLE.

BUT HE'S SO UGLY.

I RATHER LIKE HIS LOOKS.

THEIR WORLD DIDN'T ALLOW THEM TO TAKE THINGS EASILY, DIDN'T ALLOW THEM TO BE SANE, VIRTUOUS, HAPPY.

BUT HE'S SO SMALL. THEY SAY SOMEONE MADE A MISTAKE WHEN HE WAS STILL IN THE BOTTLE--PUT ALCOHOL INTO HIS BLOOD SURROGATE. THAT'S WHY HE'S SO STUNTED.

WHAT NONSENSE!

WHAT WITH MOTHERS AND LOVERS . . .

WHAT WITH THE PROHIBITIONS THEY WERE NOT CONDITIONED TO OBEY . . .

WHAT WITH THE TEMPTATIONS AND LONELY REMORSES . . .

FANNY'S A NICE GIRL TOO.

NOT NEARLY AS PNEUMATIC AS LENINA. OH, NOT NEARLY.

WHAT WITH ALL THE DISEASES AND THE ENDLESS ISOLATING PAIN . . .

YOU'RE HOPELESS, LENINA, I GIVE YOU UP.

WHAT WITH THE UNCERTAINTIES AND THE POVERTY--THEY WERE FORCED TO FEEL STRONGLY.

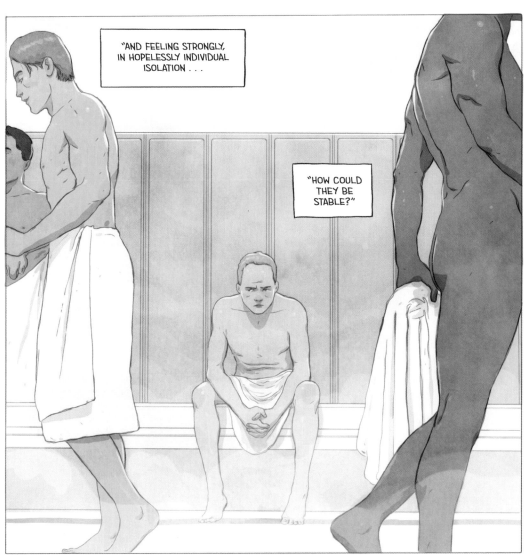

"AND FEELING STRONGLY, IN HOPELESSLY INDIVIDUAL ISOLATION . . .

"HOW COULD THEY BE STABLE?"

ONE OF THESE DAYS YOU'LL GET INTO TROUBLE.

CRYING: MY BABY, MY MOTHER, MY ONLY, ONLY LOVE. GROANING: MY SIN, MY TERRIBLE GOD; SCREAMING WITH PAIN, MUTTERING WITH FEVER, BEMOANING OLD AGE AND POVERTY . . .

FORTUNATE YOUTH! NO PAINS HAVE BEEN SPARED TO MAKE YOUR LIVES EMOTIONALLY EASY--TO PRESERVE YOU, SO FAR AS POSSIBLE, FROM HAVING ANY EMOTIONS AT ALL.

I DO LOVE HAVING NEW

OUR ANCESTORS WERE SO SHORTSIGHTED THAT WHEN THE FIRST REFORMERS CAME ALONG AND OFFERED TO DELIVER THEM FROM THOSE HORRIBLE EMOTIONS, THEY WOULDN'T HAVE ANYTHING TO DO WITH THEM.

...NG IS BETTER THAN MENDING
ENDING IS BETTER THAN MENDING
...ENDING IS BETTER THAN MEND...

NO TO ECTOGENESIS. THERE WAS SOMETHING CALLED CHRISTIANITY.

"WOMEN WERE FORCED TO GO ON BEING VIVIPAROUS."

SHNK
SHNK
SHNK
SHNK

SLEEP-TEACHING WAS PROHIBITED. THERE WAS SOMETHING CALLED LIBERALISM. SPEECHES ABOUT LIBERTY OF THE SUBJECT.

"FREEDOM TO BE A ROUND PEG IN A SQUARE HOLE . . ."

AND THE CASTE SYSTEM. CONSTANTLY PROPOSED, CONSTANTLY REJECTED. THERE WAS SOMETHING CALLED DEMOCRACY . . .

"AS THOUGH HUMAN BEINGS WERE MORE THAN PHYSICO-CHEMICALLY EQUAL."

HE DOES LOOK GLUM.

LET'S BAIT HIM.

THEN THE NINE YEARS' WAR BEGAN IN A.F. 141. PHOSGENE, CHLOROPICRIN, ETHYL IODOACETATE, DIPHENYLCYANARSINE, TRICHLORMETHYL . . .

GLUM, MARX, GLUM.

WHAT YOU NEED IS A GRAM OF SOMA.

. . . CHLOROFORMATE, DICHLORETHYL SULPHIDE, HYDROCYANIC ACID . . .

THE MORE STITCHES, THE LESS RICHES THE MORE STITCHES, THE

. . . THE GREAT ECONOMIC COLLAPSE . . .

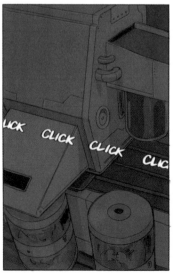

CLICK CLICK CLICK CLICK

. . . CHOICE BETWEEN WORLD CONTROL AND DESTRUCTION.

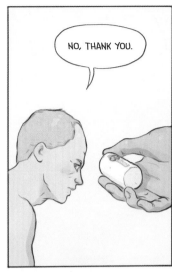

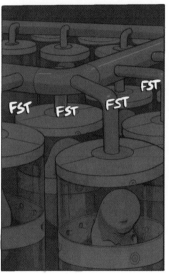

BACK TO CULTURE. YOU CAN'T CONSUME MUCH IF YOU SIT STILL AND READ.

AAAAAAAA AAAAAAA AAAA

. . . EIGHT HUNDRED SIMPLE LIFERS MOWED DOWN BY MACHINE GUNS AT GOLDERS GREEN . . .

SHNK SHNK SHNK SHNK SHN

. . . THE FAMOUS BRITISH MUSEUM MASSACRE. TWO THOUSAND CULTURE FANS GASSED WITH DICHLORETHYL SULPHIDE . . .

I LOVE NEW CLOTHES, I LOVE NEW CLOTHES, I LOVE NEW CLOTHES

. . . ACCOMPANIED BY A CAMPAIGN AGAINST THE PAST; BY THE CLOSING OF MUSEUMS, THE BLOWING UP OF HISTORICAL MONUMENTS . . .

". . . SUPPRESSION OF ALL BOOKS PUBLISHED BEFORE A.F. 150."

BIP

NO. THANK YOU.

THERE WERE SOME THINGS CALLED PYRAMIDS . . .

BIP

. . . A MAN CALLED SHAKESPEARE . . .

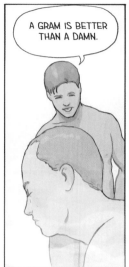

A GRAM IS BETTER THAN A DAMN.

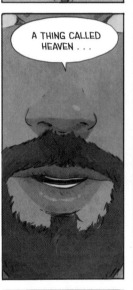

A THING CALLED HEAVEN . . .

AAAA

AAA

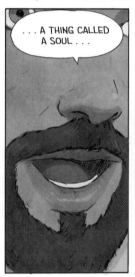

. . . A THING CALLED A SOUL . . .

OOOOOOOO

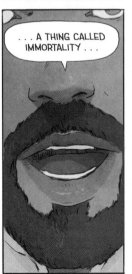

. . . A THING CALLED IMMORTALITY . . .

BIP

. . . ENORMOUS QUANTITIES OF ALCOHOL, MORPHIA, AND COCAINE . . .

DAMN YOU.

IN THE END, THE CONTROLLERS REALIZED THAT FORCE WAS NO GOOD. THE SLOWER BUT INFINITELY SURER METHODS OF ECTOGENISIS, NEO-PAVLOVIAN CONDITIONING, AND HYPNOPAEDIA WERE AT LAST MADE USE OF.

AND NOW WE HAVE THE WORLD STATE. AND FORD'S DAY CELEBRATIONS, AND COMMUNITY SINGS, AND SOLIDARITY SERVICES.

DAMN YOU, DAMN YOU.

IN A.F. 178 TWO THOUSAND PHARMACOLOGISTS AND BIOCHEMISTS WERE SUBSIDIZED.

HOITY-TOITY.

SIX YEARS LATER IT WAS BEING PRODUCED COMMERCIALLY.

IDIOTS!

EUPHORIC, NARCOTIC, PLEASANTLY HALLUCINANT.

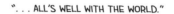

". . . ALL'S WELL WITH THE WORLD."

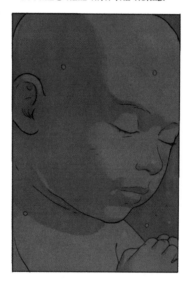

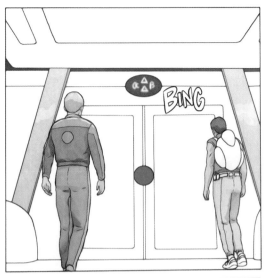

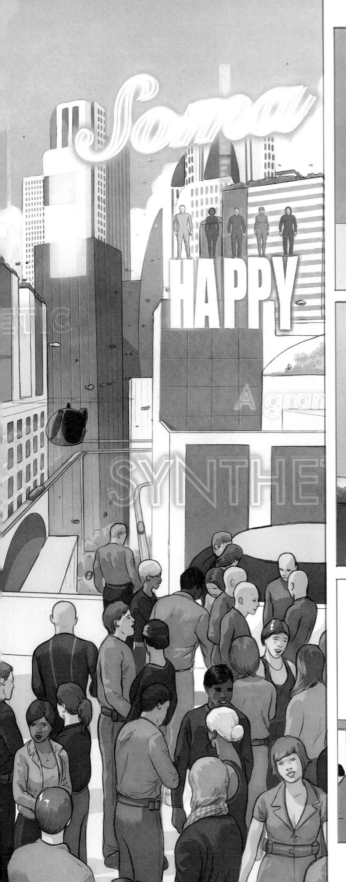

I SUPPOSE WE TAKE THE BLUE PACIFIC ROCKET?

DOES IT START FROM THE CHARING-T TOWER? OR IS IT HAMPSTEAD?

ISN'T IT BEAUTIFUL.

SIMPLY PERFECT FOR OBSTACLE GOLF!

AND NOW I MUST FLY, BERNARD. HENRY GETS CROSS IF I KEEP HIM WAITING.

LET ME KNOW IN GOOD TIME ABOUT THE DATE.

I SHOULD SAY SHE WAS PRETTY!

PNEUMATIC TOO.

. . .

BUT, I SAY, YOU DO LOOK GLUM!

WHAT YOU NEED IS A GRAM OF . . .

BUT, I SAY!

WHATEVER CAN BE THE MATTER WITH THE FELLOW?

MUST BE TRUE WHAT THEY SAY ABOUT THE ALCOHOL IN HIS BLOOD SURROGATE.

TOUCHED HIS BRAIN, I SUPPOSE.

FOUR
MINUTES
LATE.

WOSH WOSH WOSH WOSH WO

WHAT A HIDEOUS
COLOR KHAKI IS. MY
WORD, I'M GLAD I'M
NOT A DELTA.

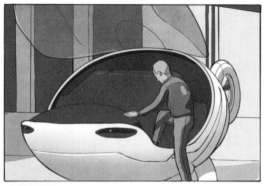

WOSH WOSH WOSH WOSH WOSH WOS

HI BERN

Favourites
Home
Fordon CC.
Helmholtz' wor...
...hambra

50

PROPAGANDA HOUSE

BOOP

TELL MR. HELMHOLTZ WATSON THAT MR. BERNARD MARX IS WAITING FOR HIM ON THE ROOF.

I HEARD THAT SHORT MAN ASKING FOR HIM JUST NOW.

HIS SECRETARY SAYS HE'S EVERY CENTIMETER THE ALPHA-PLUS.

BING

AND ONE OF THE BEST EMOTIONAL ENGINEERS.

HE'S WRITTEN COUNTLESS FEELIES. WONDERFUL KNACK FOR SLOGANS AND HYPNOPAEDIC RHYMES.

ESCALATOR SQUASH CHAMPION, TOO. APPARENTLY HE'S HAD OVER SIX HUNDRED DIFFERENT GIRLS IN JUST THE LAST FOUR YEARS!

BING

OH, HELMHOLTZ DARLING!

DO COME JOIN US FOR A PICNIC ON EXMOOR.

NO, NO.

OH, DO COME, IT'LL BE SUCH--

NO, I'M BUSY.

WE AREN'T INVITING ANY OTHER MEN.

I'M TAKING LENINA CROWNE TO NEW MEXICO WITH ME.

ARE YOU?

THIS LAST WEEK OR TWO I'VE BEEN CUTTING ALL MY COMMITTEES AND ALL MY GIRLS. YOU CAN IMAGINE WHAT A HULLABALOO THEY'VE BEEN MAKING ABOUT IT AT THE COLLEGE.

STILL, IT'S BEEN WORTH IT, I THINK. THE EFFECTS . . .

WELL, THEY'RE ODD. VERY ODD.

DO YOU EVER FEEL . . .

. . . AS THOUGH YOU HAD SOMETHING INSIDE YOU THAT WAS ONLY WAITING FOR YOU TO GIVE IT A CHANCE TO COME OUT?

SOME SORT OF EXTRA POWER THAT YOU AREN'T USING--YOU KNOW, LIKE ALL THE WATER THAT GOES DOWN THE FALLS INSTEAD OF GOING THROUGH THE TURBINES?

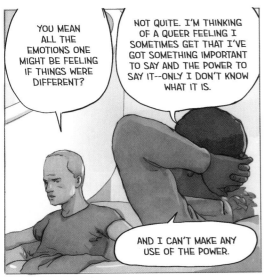

YOU MEAN ALL THE EMOTIONS ONE MIGHT BE FEELING IF THINGS WERE DIFFERENT?

NOT QUITE. I'M THINKING OF A QUEER FEELING I SOMETIMES GET THAT I'VE GOT SOMETHING IMPORTANT TO SAY AND THE POWER TO SAY IT--ONLY I DON'T KNOW WHAT IT IS.

AND I CAN'T MAKE ANY USE OF THE POWER.

IF THERE WAS SOME DIFFERENT WAY OF WRITING . . .

OR ELSE SOMETHING ELSE TO WRITE ABOUT.

A gram in time saves nine!

SYNCHRO

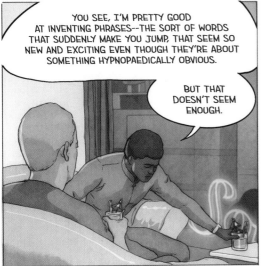

YOU SEE, I'M PRETTY GOOD AT INVENTING PHRASES--THE SORT OF WORDS THAT SUDDENLY MAKE YOU JUMP, THAT SEEM SO NEW AND EXCITING EVEN THOUGH THEY'RE ABOUT SOMETHING HYPNOPAEDICALLY OBVIOUS.

BUT THAT DOESN'T SEEM ENOUGH.

I FEEL I COULD DO SOMETHING MUCH MORE IMPORTANT. YES, AND MORE INTENSE, MORE VIOLENT.

BUT WHAT?

AND HOW CAN ONE BE VIOLENT ABOUT THE SORT OF THINGS ONE'S EXPECTED TO WRITE ABOUT? CAN YOU MAKE WORDS REALLY PIERCING WHEN YOU'RE WRITING ABOUT A COMMUNITY SING, OR THE LATEST IMPROVEMENT IN SCENT ORGANS?

CAN YOU SAY SOMETHING ABOUT NOTHING? THAT'S WHAT IT FINALLY BOILS DOWN TO. I TRY AND I TRY . . .

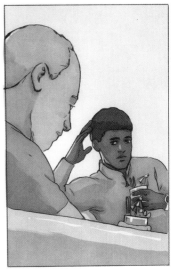

55

HMM?

I'M SORRY.

I SUPPOSE I'VE GOT THINGS ON MY NERVES A BIT.

IF YOU KNEW WHAT I'D HAD TO PUT UP WITH RECENTLY.

IF YOU ONLY KNEW.

ANYWAY, I'D BEST BE GOING. IT'S MY SOLIDARITY SERVICE THIS EVENING AT THE FORDSON COMMUNITY SINGERY.

WHAT WERE YOU PLAYING THIS AFTERNOON? OBSTACLE OR ELECTRO-MAGNETIC?

NEITHER.

THE GROUP IS NOW COMPLETE . . .

. . . THE SOLIDARITY CIRCLE PERFECT AND WITHOUT FLAW.

I DRINK TO THE GREATER BEING.

COME, GREATER BEING, SOCIAL FRIEND, ANNIHILATING TWELVE-IN-ONE!

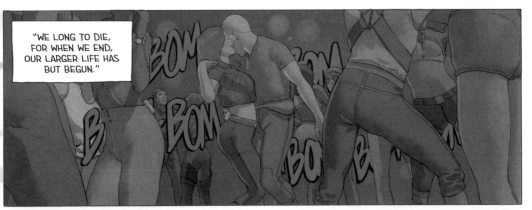

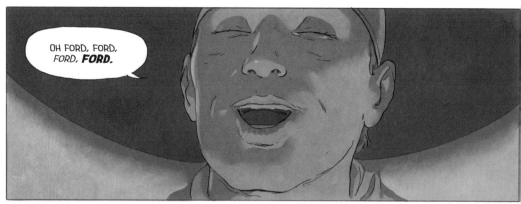

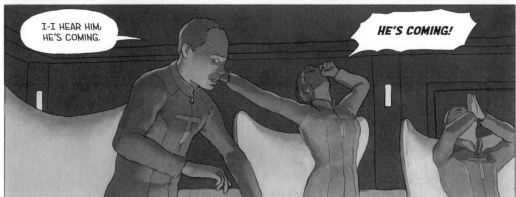

I-I HEAR HIM; HE'S COMING.

HE'S COMING!

ORGY-PORGY!

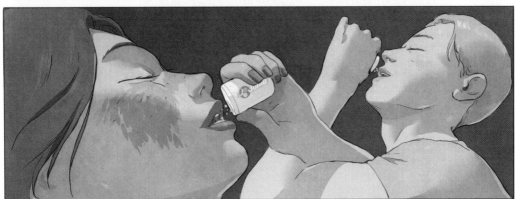

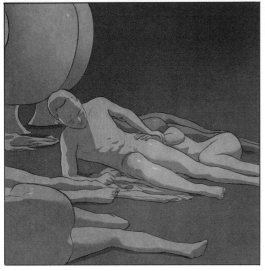

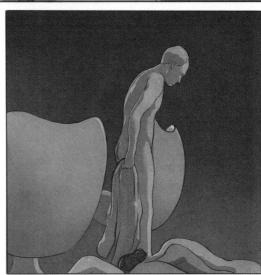

WASN'T IT WONDERFUL?

QUITE WONDERFUL.

HE'S JUST SO ODD. ODD, ODD, ODD.

BERNARD?

I'VE HAD HALF A MIND TO CANCEL OUR NEW MEXICO HOLIDAY, AND GO INSTEAD TO THE NORTH POLE WITH BENITO HOOVER.

OH YES?

TROUBLE IS I WENT TO THE NORTH POLE WITH GEORGE EDZEL LAST SUMMER AND FOUND THE PLACE PRETTY GRIM.

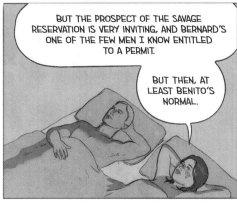

BUT THE PROSPECT OF THE SAVAGE RESERVATION IS VERY INVITING, AND BERNARD'S ONE OF THE FEW MEN I KNOW ENTITLED TO A PERMIT.

BUT THEN, AT LEAST BENITO'S NORMAL.

YOU CAN'T TEACH A RHINOCEROS TRICKS. SOME MEN ARE ALMOST RHINOCEROSES; THEY DON'T RESPOND PROPERLY TO CONDITIONING.

POOR DEVILS! BERNARD'S ONE OF THEM.

LUCKILY FOR HIM, HE'S PRETTY GOOD AT HIS JOB. OTHERWISE THE DIRECTOR WOULD NEVER HAVE KEPT HIM.

HOWEVER, I THINK HE'S PRETTY HARMLESS.

COMMUNITY
IDENTITY
STABILITY

OH BERNARD!

LENINA, I--

IT'S A BEAUTIFUL AFTERNOON. I WONDERED IF YOU'D LIKE TO JOIN ME FOR A SWIM AT TORQUAY?

TOO CROWDED, I SHOULD THINK, ON A DAY LIKE THIS.

THEN WHAT ABOUT A ROUND OF ELECTROMAGNETIC GOLF AT ST. ANDREWS?

ELECTRO-MAGNETIC GOLF IS SUCH A WASTE OF TIME.

THEN WHAT'S TIME FOR?

LET'S . . . LET'S GO FOR A WALK, IN THE LAKE DISTRICT. ALONE.

BUT, BERNARD, WE SHALL BE ALONE ALL NIGHT.

I MEANT, ALONE FOR TALKING.

TALKING? BUT WHAT ABOUT?

TELL YOU WHAT, LET'S GO TO AMSTERDAM. FANNY HAS SPARE TICKETS TO THE SEMI-DEMI-FINALS OF THE WOMEN'S HEAVYWEIGHT WRESTLING CHAMPIONSHIP!

THE WOMEN'S HEAVYWEIGHT WRESTLING CHAMPIONSHIP.

IT'LL BE SUCH FUN!

I'LL GO TALK TO HER RIGHT AWAY. MEET YOU ON THE ROOF?

ROUND 3

A GRAM IN TIME SAVES NINE.

I'D RATHER BE MYSELF.

MYSELF AND NASTY.

ONE CUBIC CENTIMETER CURES TEN GLOOMY SENTIMENTS.

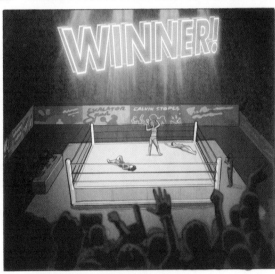

OH, FOR FORD'S SAKE, BE QUIET!

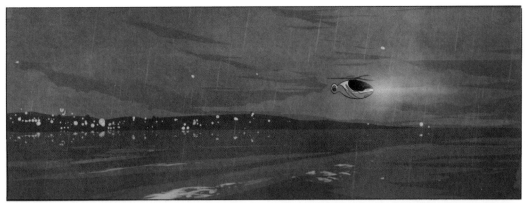

BIP

BERNARD? WHY'VE WE STOPPED?

LOOK.

BUT IT'S HORRIBLE.

LET'S PUT SOME MUSIC ON.

WAIT, I WANT TO LOOK AT THE SEA IN PEACE.

IT'S HORRIBLE.

IT MAKES ME FEEL AS THOUGH . . .

AS THOUGH I WERE MORE ME, IF YOU SEE WHAT I MEAN. NOT JUST A CELL IN THE SOCIAL BODY.

DOESN'T IT MAKE YOU FEEL LIKE THAT, LENINA?

DON'T YOU WISH YOU WERE FREE?

I AM FREE! FREE TO HAVE THE MOST WONDERFUL TIME.

EVERYBODY'S HAP--

YES, "EVERYBODY'S HAPPY NOW."

WE BEGIN GIVING CHILDREN THAT AT FIVE. BUT WOULDN'T YOU LIKE TO BE FREE AND HAPPY IN SOME OTHER WAY, LENINA?

IN YOUR OWN WAY, FOR EXAMPLE; NOT IN EVERYBODY ELSE'S WAY.

I DON'T KNOW WHAT YOU MEAN.

YOU'RE SAYING THE MOST AWFUL THINGS. OH, DO LET'S GO BACK, BERNARD. I DO SO HATE IT HERE.

I THOUGHT WE'D BE MORE . . . MORE *TOGETHER* HERE--WITH NOTHING BUT THE SEA AND MOON.

MORE TOGETHER THAN IN THAT CROWD, OR EVEN IN MY ROOMS. DON'T YOU UNDERSTAND THAT?

I DON'T UNDERSTAND ANYTHING. NOTHING. LEAST OF ALL WHY YOU DON'T TAKE SOMA WHEN YOU HAVE THESE DREADFUL IDEAS OF YOURS.

ALL RIGHT, WE'LL GO BACK.

HA HA HA HA

FEELING BETTER?

AA HAHA HAHAHA HA HA HA HA HA HAAA

A HA HA HA HA HA HA HA HA HA HA HA HA HA

80

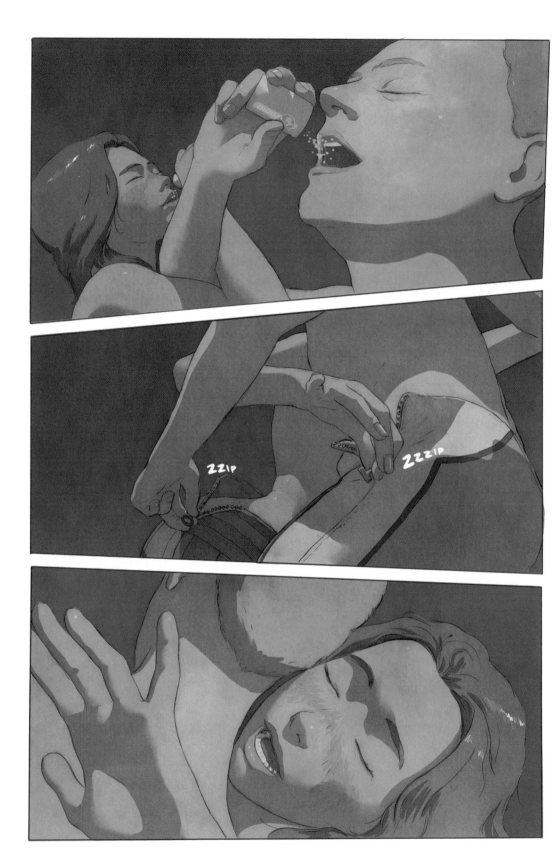

WELL, DID YOU THINK IT WAS FUN?

MM-HMM.

EVERYONE SAYS I'M AWFULLY PNEUMATIC.

AWFULLY.

BUT YOU DON'T THINK I'M *TOO* PLUMP DO YOU?

NO.

YOU THINK I'M ALL RIGHT?

IN EVERY WAY?

PERFECT.

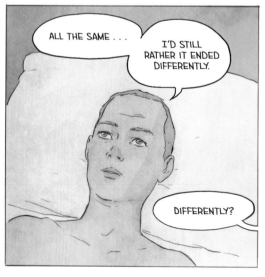

ALL THE SAME . . .

I'D STILL RATHER IT ENDED DIFFERENTLY.

DIFFERENTLY?

I DIDN'T WANT IT TO END WITH OUR GOING TO BED.

NOT AT ONCE, NOT THE FIRST DAY.

BUT THEN WHAT . . .?

I'D LIKE TO TRY THE EFFECT OF ARRESTING MY IMPULSES.

NEVER PUT OFF TILL TOMORROW THE FUN YOU CAN HAVE TODAY.

TWO HUNDRED REPETITIONS, TWICE A WEEK, FROM FOURTEEN TO SIXTEEN AND A HALF.

I WANT TO KNOW WHAT PASSION IS. I WANT TO FEEL SOMETHING STRONGLY.

WHEN THE INDIVIDUAL FEELS, THE COMMUNITY REELS.

WELL, WHY SHOULDN'T IT REEL A BIT?

BERNARD!

WE'RE ADULTS INTELLECTUALLY AND DURING WORKING HOURS. INFANTS WHERE FEELING AND DESIRE ARE CONCERNED.

I DON'T UNDERSTAND.

I KNOW YOU DON'T. THAT'S WHY WE WENT TO BED TOGETHER YESTERDAY.

BUT IT WAS FUN, WASN'T IT?

OH THE GREATEST FUN.

COMMUNITY IDENTITY STABILITY

A PERMIT FOR YOU TO INITIAL, DIRECTOR.

FOR THE NEW MEXICO RESERVATION?

THAT'S RIGHT.

HMM.

YOU KNOW, I HAD THE SAME IDEA WHEN I WAS YOUR AGE. MUST BE TWENTY-FIVE YEARS AGO NOW.

I WANTED TO HAVE A LOOK AT THE SAVAGES. GOT A PERMIT FOR NEW MEXICO AND WENT THERE FOR MY SUMMER HOLIDAY.

WITH THE GIRL I WAS HAVING AT THE MOMENT. SHE WAS A BETA-MINUS, AND I THINK . . .

I THINK SHE HAD YELLOW HAIR.

ANYWAY, SHE WAS PNEUMATIC, PARTICULARLY PNEUMATIC, I REMEMBER THAT.

"WELL, WE WENT THERE, AND WE LOOKED AT THE SAVAGES, AND WE RODE ABOUT ON HORSES AND ALL THAT.

"AND THEN--IT WAS ALMOST THE LAST DAY OF MY LEAVE-- THEN . . . WELL, SHE GOT LOST.

"WE'D GONE RIDING UP ONE OF THOSE REVOLTING MOUNTAINS, AND IT WAS HORRIBLY HOT AND OPPRESSIVE, AND AFTER LUNCH WE WENT TO SLEEP.

"OR AT LEAST I DID. SHE MUST HAVE GONE FOR A WALK, ALONE. AT ANY RATE, WHEN I WOKE UP, SHE WASN'T THERE.

KERAKKKO

"AND THE MOST FRIGHTFUL THUNDERSTORM I'D EVER SEEN WAS JUST BURSTING UPON US.

"IT POURED AND ROARED AND FLASHED. THE HORSES BROKE LOOSE AND RAN AWAY.

"I SEARCHED AND I SHOUTED AND I SEARCHED."

SHE MUST HAVE FALLEN INTO A GULLY SOMEWHERE; OR BEEN EATEN BY A MOUNTAIN LION. FORD KNOWS.

IT UPSET ME VERY MUCH AT THE TIME. MORE THAN IT OUGHT TO HAVE DONE, I DARE SAY. BECAUSE, AFTER ALL, IT'S THE SORT OF ACCIDENT THAT COULD HAVE HAPPENED TO ANYONE; AND, OF COURSE, THE SOCIAL BODY PERSISTS THOUGH THE COMPONENT CELLS MAY CHANGE.

I ACTUALLY DREAM ABOUT IT SOMETIMES. DREAM OF BEING WOKEN BY THAT PEAL OF THUNDER AND FINDING HER GONE.

YOU MUST HAVE HAD A TERRIBLE SHOCK.

DON'T IMAGINE THAT I'D HAD ANY INDECOROUS RELATION WITH THE GIRL. NOTHING EMOTIONAL, NOTHING LONG-DRAWN.

IT WAS ALL PERFECTLY HEALTHY AND NORMAL.

I REALLY DON'T KNOW WHY I BORED YOU WITH THIS TRIVIAL ANECDOTE.

AND I SHOULD LIKE TO TAKE THIS OPPORTUNITY, MR. MARX, OF SAYING THAT I'M NOT AT ALL PLEASED WITH THE REPORTS OF YOUR BEHAVIOR OUTSIDE WORKING HOURS.

YOU MAY SAY THIS IS NONE OF MY BUSINESS. BUT I HAVE THE GOOD NAME OF THE CENTER TO THINK OF. MY WORKERS MUST BE ABOVE SUSPICION, PARTICULARLY THOSE OF THE HIGHEST CASTES.

ALPHAS ARE SO CONDITIONED THAT THEY DO NOT HAVE TO BE INFANTILE IN THEIR EMOTIONAL BEHAVIOR. BUT THAT IS ALL THE MORE REASON FOR THEIR MAKING A SPECIAL EFFORT TO CONFORM.

IT IS THEIR DUTY TO BE INFANTILE, EVEN AGAINST THEIR INCLINATION.

AND SO, MR. MARX, I GIVE YOU FAIR WARNING . . .

IF I EVER HEAR AGAIN OF ANY LAPSE FROM A PROPER STANDARD OF INFANTILE DECORUM, I SHALL ASK FOR YOUR TRANSFERENCE TO A SUB-CENTER-- PREFERABLY TO ICELAND.

GOOD MORNING.

. . . HA HA, HE NO DOUBT THOUGHT HE'D TAUGHT ME A LESSON.

BUT I FELT POSITIVELY ELATED. I FELT SIGNIFICANT! BESIDES, ICELAND'S AN EMPTY THREAT. PEOPLE AREN'T TRANSFERRED FOR THINGS LIKE THAT.

SO I SIMPLY TOLD HIM TO GO TO THE BOTTOMLESS PAST AND MARCHED OUT OF THE ROOM.

AND THAT WAS THAT.

... FIVE HUNDRED AND SIXTY THOUSAND SQUARE KILOMETERS, DIVIDED INTO FOUR DISTINCT SUB-RESERVATIONS, EACH SURROUNDED BY A HIGH-TENSION WIRE FENCE.

SUPPLIED WITH CURRENT FROM THE GRAND CANYON HYDROELECTRIC STATION.

NEW MEXICO
SAVAGE RESERVATION
PERMIT-HOLDERS ONLY

UPWARDS OF FIVE THOUSAND KILOMETERS OF FENCING AT SIXTY THOUSAND VOLTS.

YOU DON'T SAY SO.

TO TOUCH THE FENCE IS INSTANT DEATH.

THERE IS NO ESCAPE FROM A SAVAGE RESERVATION.

THOSE WHO ARE BORN IN THE RESERVATION--AND REMEMBER THAT CHILDREN STILL ARE BORN, YES, ACTUALLY BORN, REVOLTING AS THAT MAY SEEM . . .

BOOP BOOP BOOP

THOSE WHO ARE BORN IN THE RESERVATION ARE DESTINED TO DIE THERE.

MESSAGE FROM HELMHOLTZ:
Thought I should let you know: DHC looking for someone to replace you. Mentioned Iceland 😬 Sorry to bring you bad news on your hols 🏖

WHAT'S THE MATTER?

I'M GOING TO BE SENT TO ICELAND.

YOU DON'T SAY--

THE DIRECTOR THREATENED, BUT I DIDN'T TAKE HIM SERIOUSLY.

I EVEN . . . I EVEN WELCOMED THE PROSPECT OF A CHANCE TO ENDURE SOME HARDSHIP, SOME PAIN, SOME AFFLICTION.

WHAT A FOOL I WAS. ICELAND, *ICELAND* . . .

WAS AND WILL MAKE ME ILL. I TAKE A GRAM AND ONLY AM.

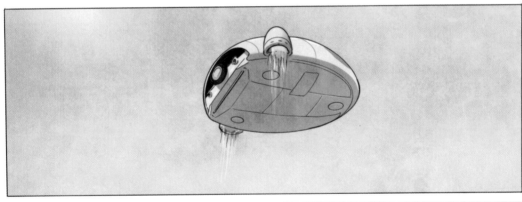

WE'RE APPROACHING THE INNERMOST PERIMETER.

MALPAIS.

THIS IS THE REST HOUSE. I'LL SHOW YOU TO YOUR GUIDE.

THERE'S A DANCE THIS AFTERNOON AT THE PUEBLO. HE'LL TAKE YOU THERE.

SHOULD BE FUNNY.

BACK TOMORROW. AND REMEMBER, THEY'RE PERFECTLY TAME SAVAGES.

THEY'VE GOT ENOUGH EXPERIENCE OF GAS BOMBS TO KNOW THEY MUSTN'T PLAY ANY TRICKS.

I WISH WE COULD HAVE BROUGHT THE PLANE. I HATE WALKING.

WHAT'S THE MATTER WITH HIM?

HE'S OLD, THAT'S ALL.

OLD?

BUT THE DIRECTOR'S OLD; LOTS OF PEOPLE ARE OLD; THEY'RE NOT LIKE THAT.

THAT'S BECAUSE WE DON'T ALLOW IT. WE DON'T PERMIT THEIR MAGNESIUM-CALCIUM RATIO TO FALL BELOW WHAT IT WAS AT THIRTY. WE GIVE THEM TRANSFUSIONS OF YOUNG BLOOD. WE KEEP THEIR METABOLISM PERMANENTLY STIMULATED.

YOUTH ALMOST UNIMPAIRED TILL SIXTY, AND THEN, CRACK! THE END.

BUT . . . HOW DO THEY LIVE LIKE THIS?

WE OUGHT NOT TO HAVE COME HERE.

THEY WOULDN'T LET ME BE THE SACRIFICE.

THEY COULD HAVE HAD TWICE AS MUCH BLOOD FROM ME. THE MULTITUDINOUS SEAS INCARNADINE.

DO YOU MEAN TO SAY THAT YOU *WANTED* TO BE HIT WITH THAT WHIP?

FOR THE SAKE OF THE PUEBLO. AND TO PLEASE POOKONG AND JESUS. AND THEN TO SHOW THAT I CAN BEAR PAIN WITHOUT CRYING OUT.

TO SHOW THAT I'M A MAN AND . . .

A-AND . . .

OH!

OH, MY DEAR, MY DEAR.

IF YOU KNEW HOW GLAD — AFTER ALL THESE YEARS!

I THOUGHT I SHOULD NEVER SEE A PIECE OF REAL ACETATE SILK AGAIN.

I SUPPOSE JOHN TOLD YOU WHAT WE'VE HAD TO SUFFER. AND NOT A GRAM OF SOMA TO BE HAD.

ONLY A DRINK OF MESCAL EVERY NOW AND THEN, WHEN POPÉ USED TO BRING IT. POPÉ IS A BOY I USED TO KNOW.

BUT IT MAKES YOU FEEL SO BAD AFTERWARDS, THE MESCAL DOES.

AND I WAS SO ASHAMED. JUST THINK OF IT: ME, A BETA--HAVING A BABY. PUT YOURSELF IN MY PLACE.

I STILL DON'T KNOW HOW IT HAPPENED, SEEING THAT I DID ALL THE MALTHUSIAN DRILL.

AND OF COURSE THERE WASN'T ANYTHING LIKE THE CHELSEA ABORTION CENTER HERE.

AH, THAT LOVELY PINK GLASS TOWER!

AND THE RIVER AT NIGHT . . .

OH, I'M SO SORRY. I REMEMBER HOW IT USED TO UPSET ME, ALL THAT DIRT, AND NOTHING BEING ASEPTIC.

"CIVILIZATION IS STERILIZATION," I USED TO TELL THEM. AND "STREPTOCOCK-GEE TO BANBURY-T, TO SEE A FINE BATHROOM AND W.C." AS THOUGH THEY WERE CHILDREN.

AND THESE CLOTHES. THIS BEASTLY WOOL ISN'T LIKE ACETATE. IT LASTS AND LASTS. AND YOU'RE SUPPOSED TO MEND IT IF IT GETS TORN. "THE MORE STITCHES, THE LESS RICHES." ISN'T THAT RIGHT? MENDING'S ANTI-SOCIAL.

IT'S LIKE LIVING WITH LUNATICS. EVERYTHING THEY DO IS MAD.

FOR INSTANCE, TAKE THE WAY THEY HAVE EACH OTHER HERE.

EVERYBODY BELONGS TO EVERYONE ELSE--DON'T THEY? DON'T THEY?

WELL, HERE NOBODY'S SUPPOSED TO BELONG TO MORE THAN ONE PERSON.

*!@?

WHY ARE THEY ANGRY WITH YOU, LINDA?

BECAUSE I BROKE SOMETHING. HOW SHOULD I KNOW HOW TO DO THEIR BEASTLY WEAVING?

BEASTLY SAVAGES.

WHAT ARE SAVAGES?

AND IF YOU HAVE PEOPLE IN THE ORDINARY WAY, THE OTHERS THINK YOU'RE WICKED AND ANTI-SOCIAL.

GO AND PLAY NOW, JOHN.

THEY HATE AND DESPISE YOU.

HA HA HA

ONCE A LOT OF WOMEN CAME AND MADE A SCENE BECAUSE THEIR MEN CAME TO SEE ME. WELL, WHY NOT?

NO, IT WAS TOO AWFUL. I CAN'T TELL YOU ABOUT IT.

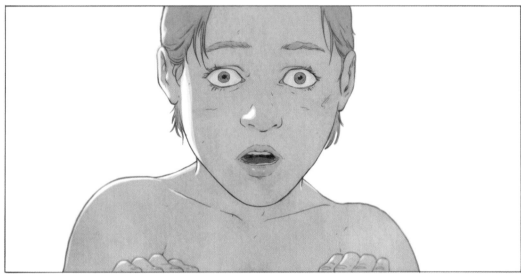

THEY'RE SO HATEFUL, THE WOMEN HERE.

MAD.

WHY DID THEY WANT TO HURT YOU, LINDA?

I DON'T KNOW. HOW SHOULD I KNOW? THEY SAID THOSE MEN WERE *THEIR* MEN.

AND OF COURSE THEY DON'T KNOW ANYTHING ABOUT MALTHUSIAN DRILL, OR BOTTLES, OR DECANTING, OR ANYTHING OF THAT SORT.

SO THEY'RE HAVING CHILDREN ALL THE TIME-- LIKE DOGS. IT'S TOO REVOLTING.

OH, DON'T CRY, LINDA. DON'T CRY.

OH, BE CAREFUL. MY SHOULDER!

AND TO THINK THAT I . . . OH, FORD, FORD, FORD!

LITTLE IDIOT!

AND YET JOHN WAS A GREAT COMFORT TO ME. I DON'T KNOW WHAT I SHOULD HAVE DONE WITHOUT HIM.

LINDA . . . OH, MOTHER, DON'T!

I'M NOT YOUR MOTHER. I WON'T BE YOUR MOTHER.

BUT LINDA . . .

TURNED INTO A SAVAGE. HAVING YOUNG ONES LIKE AN ANIMAL . . .

THERE WERE HAPPY TIMES, WEREN'T THERE, JOHN? WHEN I USED TO TELL YOU ABOUT THE CIVILIZED WORLD . . .

LITTLE BEAST!

DON'T, LINDA.

ABOUT PINK AND GREEN AND BLUE AND SILVER HOUSES AS HIGH AS MOUNTAINS, AND EVERYONE HAPPY AND NO ONE EVER SAD OR ANGRY . . .

PLEASE . . .

AND EVERYONE BELONGING TO EVERYONE ELSE. AND NO NASTY SMELLS, NO DIRT AT ALL.

AND YOU CAN GO FLYING WHENEVER YOU LIKE?

HIC

WHENEVER YOU LIKE.

I ALSO LISTENED TO THE OLD MEN OF THE PUEBLO, AND HEARD ABOUT AWONAWILONA, WHO MADE THE WORLD OUT OF FOG; OF EARTH MOTHER AND SKY FATHER; OF AHAIYUTA AND MARSAILEMA . . .

"... THE TWINS OF WAR AND CHANCE; OF JESUS AND POOKONG ..."

"... OF MARY AND ETSANATLEHI ..."

THE WOMAN WHO MAKES HERSELF YOUNG AGAIN ...

"AT NIGHT I WOULD LIE IN BED, THINKING OF HEAVEN AND LONDON AND OUR LADY OF ACOMA ..."

"AND THE ROWS AND ROWS OF BABIES IN CLEAN BOTTLES AND JESUS FLYING UP AND LINDA FLYING UP AND THE GREAT DIRECTOR OF WORLD HATCHERIES AND AWONAWILONA."

I DID MANAGE TO CONDITION HIM A LITTLE.

I TAUGHT HIM TO READ. THE OTHER BOYS WERE BEASTLY TO HIM.

MY MUM KICKED MY DAD OUT THANKS TO YOUR WHORE OF A MOTHER!

SHE'S A DRUNKEN SLU--

AH!

117

POPÉ LEFT SOMETHING FOR YOU. A BOOK.

IT WAS LYING IN ONE OF THE CHESTS OF THE ANTELOPE KIVA.

IT'S SUPPOSED TO HAVE BEEN THERE FOR HUNDREDS OF YEARS. I EXPECT IT'S TRUE, BECAUSE I LOOKED AT IT, AND IT SEEMED TO BE FULL OF NONSENSE.

UNCIVILIZED. STILL, IT'LL BE GOOD ENOUGH FOR YOU TO PRACTICE YOUR READING ON.

William Shakespeare
COMPLETE WORKS

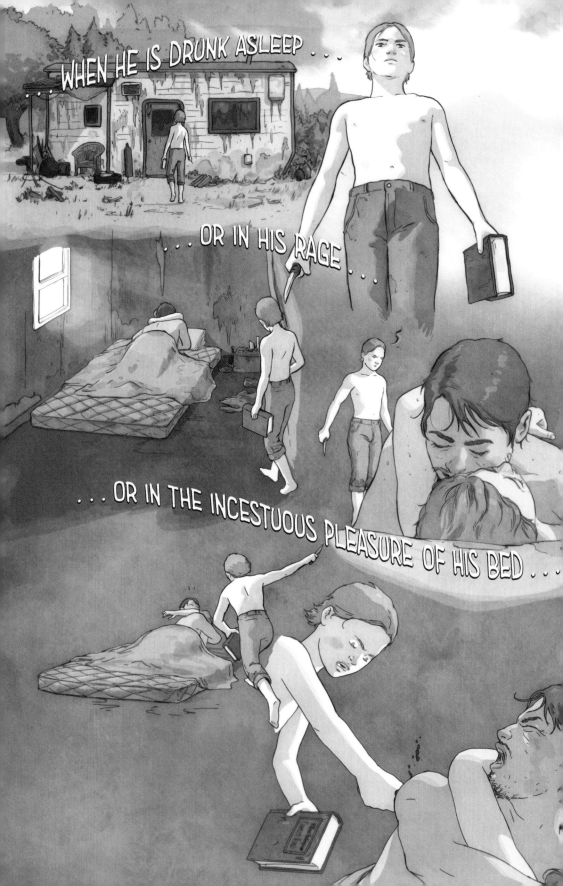

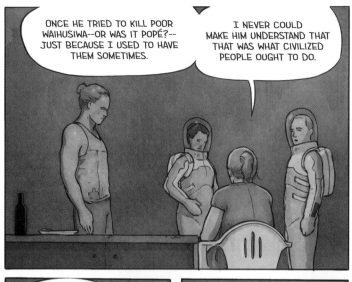

ONCE HE TRIED TO KILL POOR WAIHUSIWA--OR WAS IT POPÉ?-- JUST BECAUSE I USED TO HAVE THEM SOMETIMES.

I NEVER COULD MAKE HIM UNDERSTAND THAT THAT WAS WHAT CIVILIZED PEOPLE OUGHT TO DO.

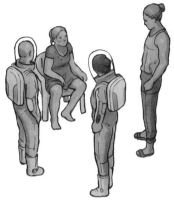

HOW WOULD YOU LIKE TO COME BACK TO LONDON WITH US?

DO YOU REALLY MEAN IT?

OF COURSE; IF I CAN GET PERMISSION, THAT IS.

TO THINK IT SHOULD BE COMING TRUE--WHAT I'VE DREAMED OF ALL MY LIFE.

DO YOU REMEMBER WHAT MIRANDA SAYS?

WHO'S MIRANDA?

O WONDER! HOW MANY GOODLY CREATURES ARE THERE HERE! HOW BEAUTEOUS MANKIND IS!

O BRAVE NEW WORLD. O BRAVE NEW WORLD THAT HAS SUCH PEOPLE IN IT!

YOU HAVE A MOST PECULIAR WAY OF TALKING SOMETIMES. AND, ANYHOW, HADN'T YOU BETTER WAIT TILL YOU ACTUALLY SEE THE NEW WORLD?

. . . I VENTURED TO THINK THAT YOUR FORDSHIP MIGHT FIND THE MATTER OF SUFFICIENT SCIENTIFIC INTEREST . . .

YES, I DO FIND IT OF SUFFICIENT SCIENTIFIC INTEREST. BRING THESE TWO INDIVIDUALS BACK TO LONDON WITH YOU.

YOUR FORDSHIP IS AWARE THAT I SHALL NEED A SPECIAL PERMIT . . .

THE NECESSARY ORDERS ARE BEING SENT TO THE WARDEN OF THE RESERVATION AT THIS MOMENT. GOOD MORNING, MR. MARX.

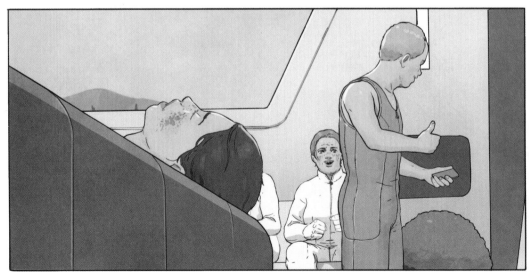

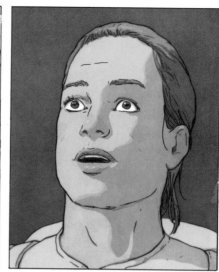

MR. MARX, WE HAVE JUST RECEIVED SPECIAL ORDERS . . .

I KNOW, I WAS TALKING TO THE CONTROLLER A MOMENT AGO.

MISS CROWNE'S GONE ON SOMA HOLIDAY. CAN HARDLY BE BACK BEFORE FIVE.

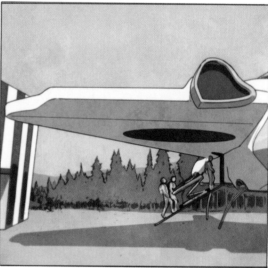

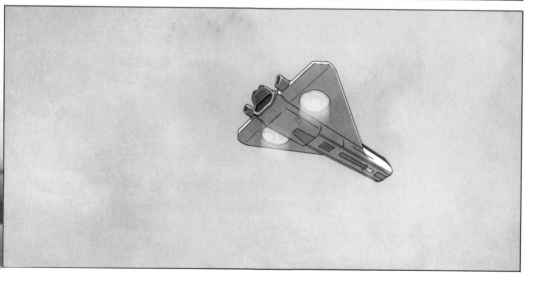

YOU ARE FIFTEEN. NOW I MAY TEACH YOU TO WORK THE CLAY.

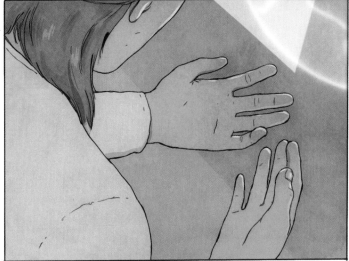

125

ARE YOU?

I THOUGHT THAT IN THE OTHER PLACE... I MEAN, LINDA ALWAYS SAID THAT NOBODY WAS EVER ALONE THERE.

I'M... RATHER DIFFERENT FROM MOST PEOPLE, I SUPPOSE.

IF ONE HAPPENS TO BE DECANTED DIFFERENT...

YES, THAT'S JUST IT. IF ONE'S DIFFERENT, ONE'S BOUND TO BE LONELY.

WHEN THE OTHER BOYS WERE SENT OUT TO SPEND THE NIGHT ON THE MOUNTAINS--YOU KNOW, WHEN YOU HAVE TO DREAM WHICH YOUR SACRED ANIMAL IS--THEY WOULDN'T LET ME GO.

I DID IT MYSELF, THOUGH. DIDN'T EAT ANYTHING FOR FIVE DAYS AND THEN WENT OUT ONE NIGHT ALONE INTO THE MOUNTAINS.

AND DID YOU DREAM OF ANYTHING?

YES. BUT I MUSTN'T TELL YOU WHAT.

ONCE I DID SOMETHING THAT NONE OF THE OTHERS DID: I STOOD ON A ROCK IN THE MIDDLE OF THE DAY, IN SUMMER, WITH MY ARMS OUT, LIKE JESUS ON THE CROSS.

WHAT ON EARTH FOR?

I WANTED TO KNOW WHAT IT WAS LIKE BEING CRUCIFIED. HANGING THERE IN THE SUN.

BUT WHY?

WHY? WELL... BECAUSE I FELT I OUGHT TO. IF JESUS COULD STAND IT.

BESIDES, I WAS UNHAPPY; THAT WAS ANOTHER REASON.

IT SEEMS A FUNNY WAY OF CURING YOUR UNHAPPINESS...

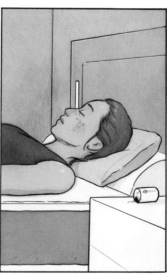

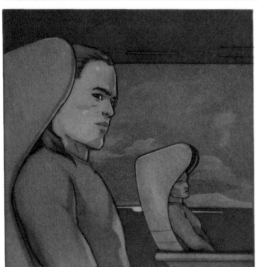

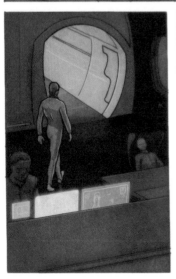

HER EYES . . .

HER EYES, HER HAIR, HER CHEEK, HER GAIT, HER VOICE. HANDLEST IN THY DISCOURSE, O! THAT HER HAND, IN WHOSE COMPARISON ALL WHITES ARE INK . . .

WRITING THEIR OWN REPROACH; TO WHOSE SOFT SEIZURE THE CYGNET'S DOWN IS HARSH . . .

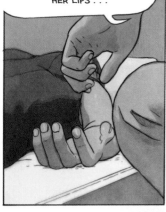

ON THE WHITE WONDER OF DEAR JULIET'S HAND, MAY SEIZE AND STEAL IMMORTAL BLESSING FROM HER LIPS . . .

WHO, EVEN IN PURE AND VESTAL MODESTY, STILL BLUSH, AS THINKING THEIR OWN KISSES SIN.

HOW BEAUTIFUL SHE IS.

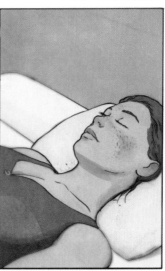

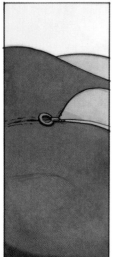

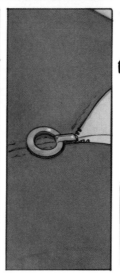

Z I P

DETESTABLE THOUGHT!

SLOUGH
CREMATORIUM

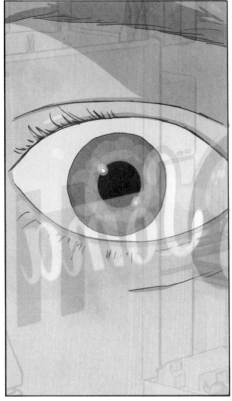

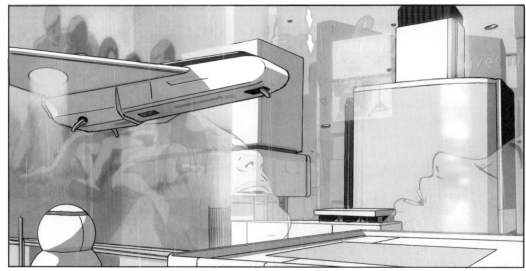

TWELVE HUNDRED AND FIFTY KILOMETERS AN HOUR. WHAT DO YOU THINK OF THAT, MR. SAVAGE?

VERY NICE.

STILL, ARIEL COULD PUT A GIRDLE ROUND THE EARTH IN FORTY MINUTES.

EH?

NOTHING.

MESSAGE FROM THE DIRECTOR OF HATCHERIES: MR. MARX TO REPORT TO THE FERTILIZING ROOM TOMORROW AT TWO THIRTY P.M. TO MEET WITH THE DHC. MESSAGE ENDS. HAVE A GREAT DAY!

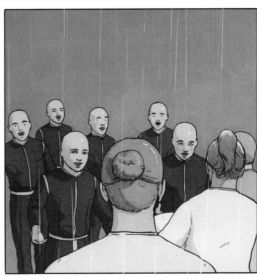

: HHEURGHH :

A gram is better

A PUBLIC EXAMPLE. IN THIS ROOM, BECAUSE IT CONTAINS MORE HIGH-CASTE WORKERS THAN ANY OTHER IN THE CENTER. I HAVE TOLD HIM TO MEET ME HERE AT HALF PAST TWO.

HE DOES HIS WORK VERY WELL.

I KNOW. BUT THAT'S ALL THE MORE REASON FOR SEVERITY. HIGH INTELLECTUAL EMINENCE CARRIES WITH IT CORRESPONDING MORAL RESPONSIBILITIES.

CONSIDER THE MATTER DISPASSIONATELY, MR. FOSTER, AND YOU WILL SEE THAT NO OFFENCE IS SO HEINOUS AS UNORTHODOXY OF BEHAVIOR.

MURDER KILLS ONLY THE INDIVIDUAL--AND, AFTER ALL, WHAT IS AN INDIVIDUAL? UNORTHODOXY STRIKES AT SOCIETY ITSELF.

GOOD MORNING, DIRECTOR!

YOU ASKED ME TO COME AND SPEAK TO YOU.

YES, MR. MARX. YOU RETURNED FROM YOUR HOLIDAY LAST NIGHT, I UNDERSTAND.

YES.

YES-S.

LADIES AND GENTLEMEN!

LADIES AND GENTLEMEN, EXCUSE ME FOR THUS INTERRUPTING YOUR LABORS. A PAINFUL DUTY CONSTRAINS ME.

THE SECURITY AND STABILITY OF SOCIETY ARE IN DANGER. YES, IN DANGER, LADIES AND GENTLEMEN.

THIS MAN--

THIS MAN WHO STANDS BEFORE YOU HERE. THIS ALPHA-PLUS TO WHOM SO MUCH HAS BEEN GIVEN, AND FROM WHOM, IN CONSEQUENCE, SO MUCH MUST BE EXPECTED . . .

THIS COLLEAGUE OF YOURS HAS GROSSLY BETRAYED THE TRUST IMPOSED IN HIM. BY HIS HERETICAL VIEWS ON SPORT AND SOMA, BY THE SCANDALOUS UNORTHODOXY OF HIS SEX LIFE . . .

BY HIS REFUSAL TO OBEY THE TEACHINGS OF OUR FORD AND BEHAVE OUT OF OFFICE HOURS "LIKE A BABE IN A BOTTLE," HE HAS PROVED HIMSELF AN ENEMY OF SOCIETY.

A SUBVERTER, LADIES AND GENTLEMEN, OF ALL ORDER AND STABILITY, A CONSPIRATOR AGAINST CIVILIZATION ITSELF.

FOR THIS REASON I PROPOSE TO DISMISS HIM WITH IGNOMINY FROM THE POST HE HAS HELD IN THIS CENTER. IN ICELAND, IN A SUB-CENTER OF THE LOWEST ORDER, HE WILL HAVE SMALL OPPORTUNITY TO LEAD OTHERS ASTRAY BY HIS UNFORDLY EXAMPLE.

MARX, CAN YOU SHOW
ANY REASON WHY I SHOULD NOT NOW EXECUTE
THE JUDGMENT PASSED UPON YOU?

YES, I CAN.

ONE MOMENT--
IT'S JUST IN THE
PASSAGE.

THERE HE IS,
LINDA.

DO YOU
THINK I DIDN'T
RECOGNIZE
HIM?

OF COURSE I KNEW YOU,
TOMAKIN, I SHOULD HAVE
KNOWN YOU ANYWHERE,
AMONG A THOUSAND.

DON'T YOU
REMEMBER ME,
TOMAKIN?

YOUR
LINDA.

T-TOMAKIN?

DON'T YOU REMEMBER?

W-WHAT'S THE MEANING OF THIS--THIS MONSTROUS . . .

. . . THIS MONSTROUS PRACTICAL JOKE!

TOMAKIN!

I'M LINDA, I'M LINDA.

YOU MADE ME HAVE A BABY.

YES, A BABY-- AND I WAS ITS MOTHER.

IT WASN'T MY FAULT, TOMAKIN. IF YOU KNEW HOW AWFUL . . . BUT HE WAS A GREAT COMFORT TO ME, ALL THE SAME.

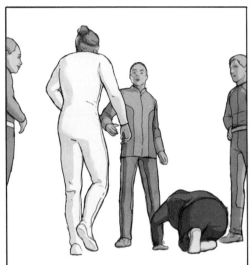

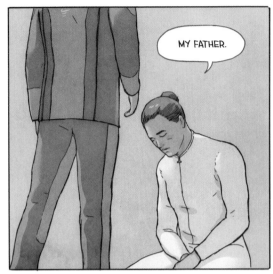
MY FATHER.

HA HA HA HA HA HA HA HA HA HA HA

MY FATHER!

OH, FORD,
TOO GOOD, TOO
GOOD.

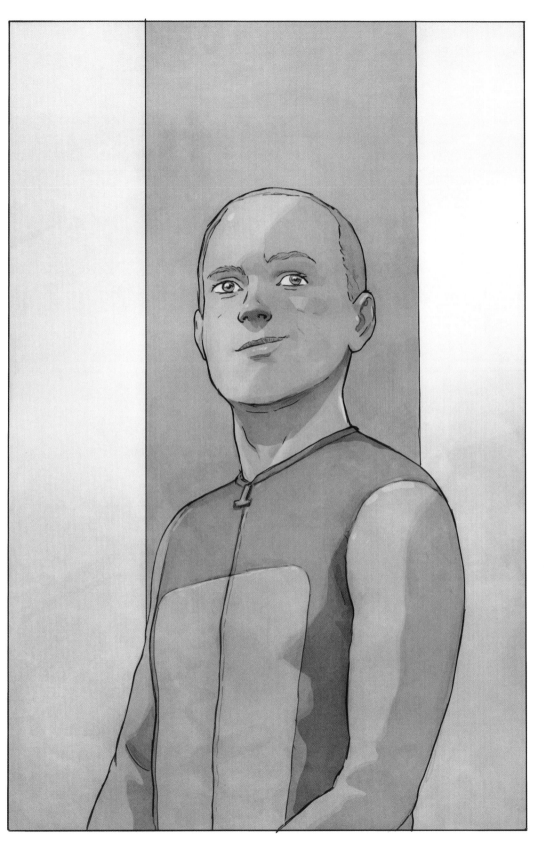

BERNARD'S
SAVAGE SOIRÉE

. . . AND I HAD SIX GIRLS LAST WEEK.

ONE ON MONDAY, TWO ON TUESDAY, TWO MORE ON FRIDAY, AND ONE ON SATURDAY.

AND THERE WERE AT LEAST A DOZEN MORE WHO WERE ONLY TOO ANXIOUS . . .

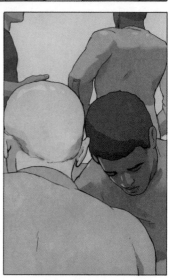

YOU'RE ENVIOUS.

I'M RATHER SAD, THAT'S ALL.

UP TO TWENTY GRAMS A DAY YOU SAY SHE'S BEEN TAKING?

WHO'S TO BLAME HER? HER SON'S BEEN A TREMENDOUS HIT, OF COURSE, BUT LINDA--WELL, WHO WANTS TO SEE A FAT, BLOTCHY OLD THING WITH MISSING TEETH? A MOTHER!

SHE'S NOT EVEN STRICTLY A REAL SAVAGE--SHE WAS HATCHED FROM A BOTTLE AND CONDITIONED JUST LIKE EVERYONE ELSE.

SO HER RETURN TO CIVILIZATION'S BEEN ONE LONG SOMA HOLIDAY, HAS IT?

WELL, IT'LL FINISH HER OFF IN A MONTH OR TWO. ONE DAY THE RESPIRATORY CENTER WILL BE PARALYZED. NO MORE BREATHING.

GOOD THING, TOO.

IN ANY CASE, UPPING HER DOSAGE IS ONLY SHORTENING HER LIFE IN ONE SENSE.

SOMA MAY MAKE YOU LOSE A FEW YEARS IN TIME, BUT THINK OF THE ENORMOUS, IMMEASURABLE DURATIONS IT CAN GIVE YOU OUT OF TIME.

EVERY SOMA HOLIDAY IS A BIT OF WHAT OUR ANCESTORS USED TO CALL ETERNITY.

I'M VERY GLAD TO HAVE HAD THIS OPPORTUNITY TO SEE AN EXAMPLE OF SENILITY IN A HUMAN BEING. THANK YOU SO MUCH FOR COMING IN.

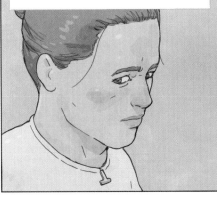

For the attention of his fordship, Mustapha Mond: A report concerning the discovery of the Savage, John, and his m—, Linda, by Bernard Marx.

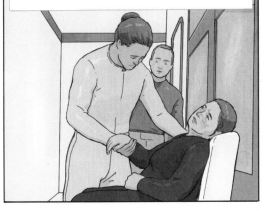

The Savage shows surprisingly little astonishment at, or awe of, civilized inventions. This is partly due, no doubt, to the fact that he has heard them talked about by the woman Linda, his m—.

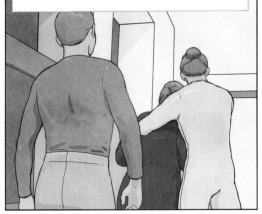

The Savage refuses to take soma and seems much distressed because the woman Linda remains permanently on soma holiday.

It is worthy of note that in spite of his m—'s senility and the extreme repulsiveness of her appearance, the Savage frequently goes to see her and appears to be much attached to her.

An interesting example of the way in which early conditioning can be made to modify and even run counter to natural impulses (in this case, the impulse to recoil from an unpleasant object).

DOES THE FOOL THINK I'M TOO SQUEAMISH TO SEE THE WORD "MOTHER" WRITTEN OUT AT FULL LENGTH?

Partly on his interest being focused on what he calls "the soul," which he persists as regarding as an entity independent of the physical environment; whereas, as I tried to point out to him . . .

HA! NOW LISTEN TO THIS: "I MUST ADMIT THAT I AGREE WITH THE SAVAGE IN FINDING CIVILIZED INFANTILITY TOO EASY OR, AS HE PUTS IT, NOT EXPENSIVE ENOUGH."

THE IDEA OF THIS CREATURE SOLEMNLY LECTURING YOU--YOU-- ABOUT THE SOCIAL ORDER REALLY IS TOO GROTESQUE.

Everybody belongs to everybody else

YOU SEEM VERY PLEASED WITH YOURSELF.

I AM PLEASED. BERNARD HAS AN UNEXPECTED ENGAGEMENT AND HE'S ASKED ME IF I'D TAKE THE SAVAGE TO THE FEELIES THIS EVENING.

LUCKY GIRL.

YOU'VE BECOME RATHER A CELEBRITY! GUEST OF HONOR AT THE APHRODITEUM CLUB, WEEKENDS WITH THE ARCH-COMMUNITY-SONGSTER OF CANTERBURY, NOW DATES WITH THE SAVAGE.

AND ALL BECAUSE OF THAT TRIP TO THE RESERVATION. NOW YOU MUST ADMIT YOU WERE WRONG ABOUT BERNARD. DON'T YOU THINK HE'S REALLY RATHER SWEET?

I MUST SAY, I WAS QUITE AGREEABLY SURPRISED.

IT'S WONDERFUL, OF COURSE. AND YET IN A WAY I FEEL AS THOUGH I WERE GETTING SOMETHING ON FALSE PRETENCES. BECAUSE THE FIRST THING EVERYONE WANTS TO KNOW IS WHAT IT'S LIKE TO MAKE LOVE TO A SAVAGE. AND I HAVE TO SAY I DON'T KNOW.

THEY DON'T BELIEVE ME, OF COURSE, BUT IT'S TRUE. I WISH IT WEREN'T. HE'S TERRIBLY GOOD-LOOKING.

BUT DOESN'T HE LIKE YOU?

SOMETIMES I THINK HE DOES AND SOMETIMES I THINK HE DOESN'T. HE ALWAYS DOES HIS BEST TO AVOID ME.

BUT SOMETIMES I CATCH HIM STARING; AND THEN--WELL, YOU KNOW HOW MEN LOOK WHEN THEY LIKE YOU.

TONIGHT AT
THE ALHAMBRA

THREE WEEKS IN
A HELICOPTER

THE ALHAMBR

TAKE HOLD OF THOSE METAL KNOBS ON THE ARMS OF YOUR CHAIR OR YOU WON'T GET ANY OF THE FEELY EFFECTS.

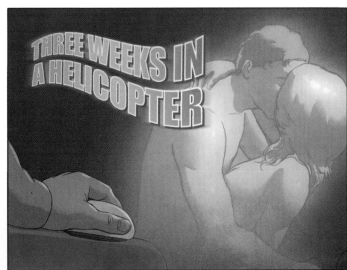

THREE WEEKS IN A HELICOPTER

?!

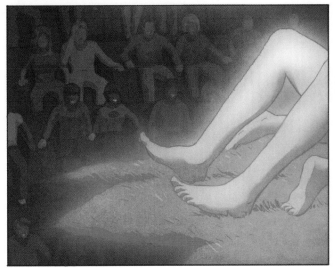

I DON'T THINK YOU OUGHT TO SEE THINGS LIKE THAT.

THINGS LIKE WHAT, JOHN?

LIKE THIS HORRIBLE FILM.

HORRIBLE? BUT I THOUGHT IT WAS LOVELY.

IT WAS BASE. IT WAS IGNOBLE.

I DON'T KNOW WHAT YOU MEAN.

GOOD NIGHT.

BUT, JOHN . . . I THOUGHT YOU WERE . . .

I MEAN, AREN'T YOU . . .?

GOOD NIGHT, LENINA.

BUT EVERYBODY'S THERE, WAITING FOR YOU.

LET THEM WAIT.

BUT YOU KNOW QUITE WELL, JOHN, I ASKED THEM ON PURPOSE TO MEET YOU.

YOU OUGHT TO HAVE ASKED *ME* FIRST WHETHER I WANTED TO MEET *THEM*.

BUT YOU ALWAYS CAME BEFORE, JOHN.

THAT'S PRECISELY WHY I DON'T WANT TO COME AGAIN.

JUST TO PLEASE ME? WON'T YOU COME TO PLEASE ME?

NO.

BUT WHAT SHALL I DO?

GO TO HELL!

BUT THE ARCH-COMMUNITY-SONGSTER IS THERE TONIGHT.

AHEM!

UH, LADIES AND GENTLEMEN . . .

LADIES AND GENTLEMEN, I DEEPLY REGRET TO INFORM YOU THAT THE SAVAGE WILL NOT BE JOINING US THIS EVENING. HE'S, UM, TEMPORARILY UNDISPOSED AND . . .

NOW, PLEASE, DO HELP YOURSELVES TO CHAMPAGNE-SURROGATE. THERE'S NO NEED TO . . .

RIDICULOUS LITTLE MAN.

TOO BAD, TOO BAD. OUR EX-DIRECTOR WAS ACTUALLY ON THE POINT OF TRANSFERRING HIM TO ICELAND.

IT REALLY IS A BIT THICK. WHEN I THINK I ACTUALLY . . .

MY FRIENDS, I THINK PERHAPS THE TIME HAS COME . . .

MUST YOU REALLY, ARCH-SONGSTER? IT'S VERY EARLY STILL.

I'D HOPED YOU WOULD . . .

MY YOUNG FRIEND, LET ME GIVE YOU A WORD OF ADVICE.

MEND YOUR WAYS, MY YOUNG FRIEND.

MEND YOUR WAYS.

LENINA, MY DEAR. COME WITH ME.

158

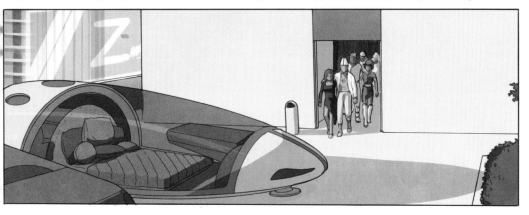

O, SHE DOTH TEACH THE TORCHES TO BURN BRIGHT . . .

IT SEEMS SHE HANGS UPON THE CHEEK OF NIGHT . . .

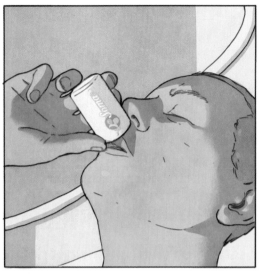

LIKE A RICH JEWEL IN AN ETHIOP'S EAR . . .

BEAUTY TOO RICH FOR USE . . .

FOR EARTH TOO DEAR.

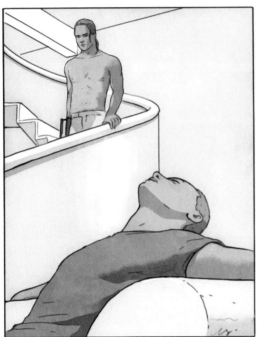

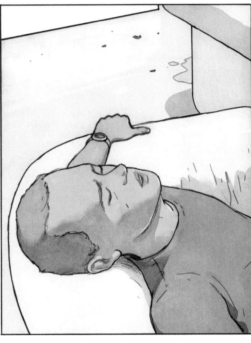

YOU'RE MORE LIKE YOU WERE AT MALPAIS. DO YOU REMEMBER WHEN WE FIRST TALKED TOGETHER?

YOU'RE LIKE WHAT YOU WERE THEN.

BECAUSE I'M UNHAPPY AGAIN, THAT'S WHY.

WELL, I'D RATHER BE UNHAPPY THAN HAVE THE SORT OF FALSE, LYING HAPPINESS YOU WERE HAVING HERE.

I LIKE THAT! WHEN IT'S YOU WHO WERE THE CAUSE OF IT ALL. REFUSING TO COME TO MY PARTY AND SO TURNING THEM ALL AGAINST ME!

I'VE ASKED MY ESTRANGED FRIEND HELMHOLTZ OVER. I THINK YOU'LL GET ON--HE, TOO, DISAPPROVES OF MY RECENT . . . WELL . . .

HE APPEARS TO HAVE FORGIVEN ME, IN ANY CASE. HE AT LEAST WAS SYMPATHETIC TO MY MISERABLE TALE.

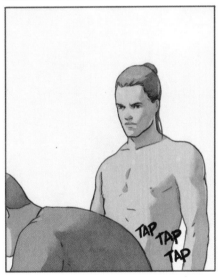

TAP TAP TAP

TAP TAP

BOOP

HELMHOLTZ, YOU'VE MET JOHN THE SAVAGE.

GOOD TO SEE YOU AGAIN, JOHN.

YOU LOOK UNCOMMONLY HAPPY, HELMHOLTZ.

THE PRINCIPAL THREATENED TO HAND ME THE IMMEDIATE SACK. I'M A MARKED MAN.

I WAS GIVING MY USUAL LECTURE ON THE USE OF RHYMES IN MORAL PROPAGANDA AND ADVERTISEMENT AND I THOUGHT THIS TIME I'D GIVE THEM ONE I'D WRITTEN MYSELF. PURE MADNESS, OF COURSE, BUT I COULDN'T RESIST IT.

IT WAS ABOUT BEING ALONE.

I WAS TRYING TO ENGINEER THEM INTO FEELING WHAT I HAD FELT WHEN I WROTE THE RHYMES. FORD! WHAT AN OUTCRY THERE WAS!

I'LL RECITE THEM TO YOU IF YOU LIKE.

"YESTERDAY'S COMMITTEE, STICKS, BUT A BROKEN DRUM . . .

"MIDNIGHT IN THE CITY, FLUTES IN A VACUUM, SHUT LIPS, SLEEPING FACES, EVERY STOPPED MACHINE . . .

"THE DUMB AND LITTERED PLACES WHERE CROWDS HAVE BEEN . . .

"ALL SILENCES REJOICE, WEEP (LOUDLY OR LOW), SPEAK--BUT WITH THE VOICE OF WHOM, I DO NOT KNOW."

WELL, I GAVE THEM THAT AS AN EXAMPLE, AND THEY REPORTED ME TO THE PRINCIPAL.

I'M NOT SURPRISED.

IT'S FLATLY AGAINST ALL THEIR SLEEP-TEACHING. REMEMBER THEY'VE HAD AT LEAST A QUARTER OF A MILLION WARNINGS AGAINST SOLITUDE.

I KNOW. BUT I THOUGHT I'D LIKE TO SEE WHAT THE EFFECTS WOULD BE.

WELL, YOU'VE SEEN NOW.

I FEEL AS THOUGH I WERE JUST BEGINNING TO HAVE SOMETHING TO WRITE ABOUT. AS THOUGH I WERE BEGINNING TO BE ABLE USE THAT POWER I FEEL I'VE GOT INSIDE ME . . .

LISTEN TO THIS.

"LET THE BIRD OF LOUDEST LAY, ON THE SOLE ARABIAN TREE, HERALD SAD AND TRUMPET BE, TO WHOSE SOUND CHASTE WINGS OBEY.

"BUT THOU SHRIEKING HARBINGER, FOUL PRECURRER OF THE FIEND, AUGUR OF THE FEVER'S END, TO THIS TROOP COME THOU NOT NEAR!

"IS THERE NO PITY SITTING IN THE CLOUDS, THAT SEES INTO THE BOTTOM OF MY GRIEF? O, SWEET MY MOTHER, CAST ME NOT AWAY!

"DELAY THIS MARRIAGE FOR A MONTH, A WEEK; OR, IF YOU DO NOT, MAKE THE BRIDAL BED IN THAT DIM MONUMENT WHERE TYBALT LIES--

HA HA HA HA HA HA!

HA HA HA HA HA HA HA HA HA HA HA

OH . . . AH, HA, I'M SORRY, JOHN--HA HA--I'M SORRY, IT'S JUST--HA!--A "MOTHER" FORCING THE "DAUGHTER" TO "MARRY" SOMEONE.

ABSURD SMUT, OF COURSE, BUT IRRESISTIBLY COMICAL. AND YET . . . OH MY . . .

AND YET I KNOW QUITE WELL ONE NEEDS RIDICULOUS, MAD SITUATIONS LIKE THAT . . .

ONE CAN'T WRITE REALLY WELL ABOUT ANYTHING ELSE.

167

LIKE TO COME TO A FEELY THIS EVENING, LENINA?

NOT THIS EVENING.

GOING OUT WITH SOMEONE ELSE?

NO.

YOU'RE NOT FEELING ILL, ARE YOU?

NO.

ANYHOW, YOU OUGHT TO GO AND SEE THE DOCTOR.

YOU MAY NEED A PREGNANCY SUBSTITUTE. OR ELSE AN EXTRA STRONG VPS TREATMENT.

SOMETIMES, YOU KNOW, THE STANDARD PASSION SURROGATE ISN'T QUITE--

OH, FOR FORD'S SAKE, SHUT UP!

TAP
TAP
TAP

BOOP

HELLO, JOHN.

YOU DON'T SEEM VERY GLAD TO SEE ME.

. . .

NOT GLAD?

NOT *GLAD*?

OH, IF ONLY YOU KNEW . . .

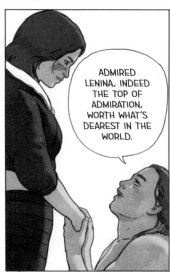

ADMIRED LENINA, INDEED THE TOP OF ADMIRATION, WORTH WHAT'S DEAREST IN THE WORLD.

OH, YOU SO PERFECT, SO PERFECT AND SO PEERLESS, ARE CREATED . . .

. . . OF EVERY CREATURE'S BEST.

THAT'S WHY I WANTED TO *DO* SOMETHING FIRST . . .

I MEAN, TO SHOW I WAS WORTHY OF YOU.

I WANTED TO DO *SOMETHING*.

WHY SHOULD YOU THINK IT NECESSARY . . .?

AT MALPAIS, YOU HAD TO BRING HER THE SKIN OF A MOUNTAIN LION--I MEAN, WHEN YOU WANTED TO MARRY SOMEONE. OR ELSE A WOLF.

THERE AREN'T ANY LIONS IN ENGLAND.

AND EVEN IF THERE WERE, PEOPLE WOULD KILL THEM OUT OF HELICOPTERS, I SUPPOSE, WITH POISON GAS OR SOMETHING.

173

I'LL DO ANYTHING. ANYTHING YOU TELL ME. THERE BE SOME SPORTS ARE PAINFUL--YOU KNOW.

BUT THEIR LABOR DELIGHT IN THEM SETS OFF.

THAT'S WHAT I FEEL. I MEAN I'D SWEEP THE FLOOR IF YOU WANTED.

WE'VE GOT VACUUM CLEANERS HERE. IT ISN'T NECESSARY.

NO, OF COURSE IT ISN'T *NECESSARY*! BUT SOME KINDS OF BASENESS ARE NOBLY UNDERGONE.

I'D LIKE TO UNDERGO SOMETHING NOBLY. DON'T YOU SEE?

BUT IF THERE *ARE* VACUUM CLEANERS . . .

THAT'S NOT THE POINT!

SO WHAT DO VACUUM CLEANERS HAVE TO DO WITH LIONS? OR LIONS WITH BEING GLAD TO SEE ME?

LISTEN, LENINA, IN MALPAIS, PEOPLE GET MARRIED.

GET WHAT?

FOR ALWAYS. THEY MAKE A PROMISE TO LIVE TOGETHER FOR ALWAYS.

WHAT A HORRIBLE IDEA!

OUTLIVING BEAUTY'S OUTWARD, WITH A MIND THAT DOTH RENEW SWIFTER THAN BLOOD DECAYS.

FOR FORD'S SAKE, JOHN, TALK SENSE!

YOU'RE DRIVING ME CRAZY. ANSWER ME THIS QUESTION: DO YOU REALLY LIKE ME, OR DON'T YOU?

I LOVE YOU MORE THAN ANYTHING IN THE WORLD.

THEN WHY DIDN'T YOU SAY SO? INSTEAD OF DRIVELING ON ABOUT VACUUM CLEANERS AND LIONS, AND MAKING ME MISERABLE FOR WEEKS.

E WEEKS IN LICOPTER

THE MURKIEST DEN, THE MOST OPPORTUNE PLACE . . .

. . . THE STRONGEST SUGGESTION OUR WORSER GENIUS CAN, SHALL NEVER MELT MINE HONOR INTO LUST.

KISS ME.

OW, JOHN, WHAT . . .? OH, DON'T, DO-ON'T--

WHORE!

WHORE!

OH!

IMPUDENT STRUMPET!

DAMNED WHORE!

WHAT IS IT?!

PLE-EASE--

GO!

A GRAM IS BETTER--

GET OUT OF MY SIGHT OR I'LL KILL YOU!

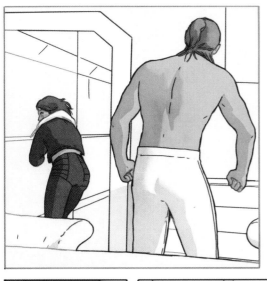
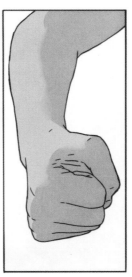

CLICK
CLICK
CLICK

BING

BOOP. BOOP. BOOP.

YES?

. . .

IF I DO NOT USURP MYSELF, I AM.

YES, DIDN'T YOU HEAR ME SAY SO? MR. SAVAGE SPEAKING.

. . .

WHAT? IS IT SERIOUS? I'LL GO AT ONCE . . .

PARK LANE HOSPITAL FOR THE DYING

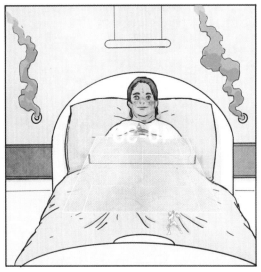
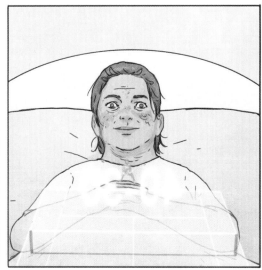

LINDA . . .

MOTHER . . .

A, B, C, VITAMIN D:
THE FAT'S IN THE LIVER,
THE COD'S IN THE
SEA.

THE TOT IS IN THE POT. THE CAT IS ON THE MAT.

OH, LOOK, LOOK!

WHATEVER IS THE MATTER WITH HER?

WHY IS SHE SO FAT?

LOOK AT HER TEETH! LOOK--

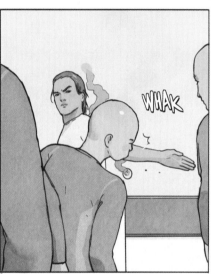

WHAK

WHAT ARE YOU DOING? I WON'T HAVE YOU STRIKING THE CHILDREN!

WELL, THEN, KEEP THEM AWAY FROM THIS BED. WHAT ARE THESE LITTLE BRATS DOING HERE AT ALL? IT'S DISGRACEFUL!

DISGRACEFUL? THEY'RE BEING DEATH-CONDITIONED. ANY MORE INTERFERENCE WITH THEIR CONDITIONING AND I'LL HAVE YOU THROWN OUT.

NOW, CHILDREN! WHO WANTS A CHOCOLATE ÉCLAIR?

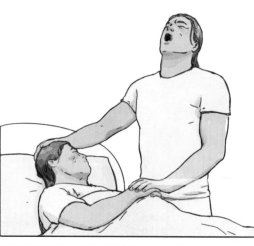

CAN'T YOU BEHAVE?

YOU'LL HAVE SET THESE POOR CHILDREN'S DEATH-CONDITIONING BACK MONTHS WITH THIS SCANDALOUS EXHIBITION.

DISGUSTING OUTCRY, AS THOUGH ANYONE MATTERED AS MUCH AS ALL THAT.

GIVE THEM THE MOST DISASTROUS IDEAS ABOUT THE SUBJECT. MIGHT UPSET THEM INTO REACTING IN THE ENTIRELY WRONG, UTTERLY ANTI-SOCIAL WAY.

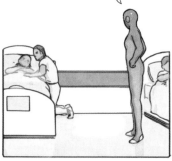

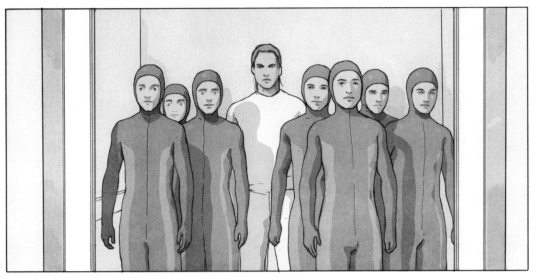

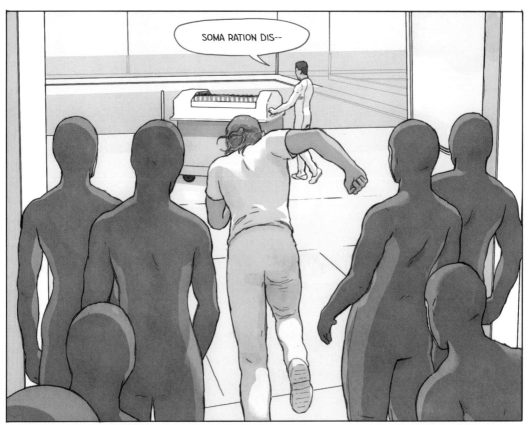

FREEDOM!

THEY'LL KILL HIM. THEY'LL . . .

FORD HELP HIM.

FORD HELPS THOSE WHO HELP THEMSELVES!

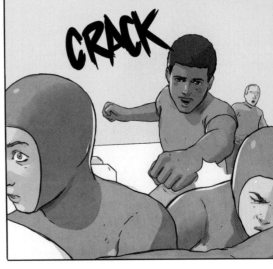

CRACK

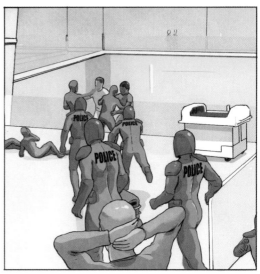

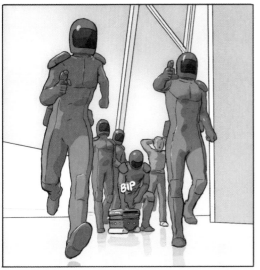

190

WORLD STATE

COMMUNITY
IDENTITY
STABILITY

OFFICES OF RESIDENT
CONTROLLER FOR
WESTERN EUROPE,
HIS FORDSHIP,
MUSTAPHA MOND

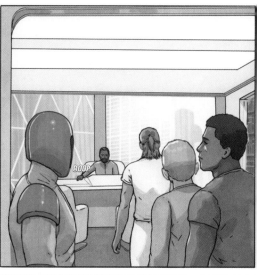

BOOP

IT'S MORE LIKE A CAFFEINE SOLUTION PARTY THAN A TRIAL.

CHEER UP, BERNARD.

SO.

YOU DON'T MUCH LIKE CIVILIZATION, MR. SAVAGE.

NO.

BUT, JOHN--

THAT WILL DO, MR. MARX.

OF COURSE, THERE ARE SOME VERY NICE THINGS. ALL THAT MUSIC IN THE AIR, FOR INSTANCE . . .

SOMETIMES A THOUSAND TWANGLING INSTRUMENTS WILL HUM ABOUT MY EARS, AND SOMETIMES VOICES.

YOU'VE READ SHAKESPEARE? I THOUGHT NOBODY KNEW ABOUT IT HERE IN ENGLAND.

ALMOST NOBODY. I'M ONE OF THE VERY FEW. IT'S PROHIBITED, YOU SEE.

BUT AS I MAKE THE LAWS HERE, I CAN ALSO BREAK THEM.

WITH IMPUNITY, MR. MARX. WHICH I'M AFRAID YOU *CAN'T* DO.

BUT WHY IS IT PROHIBITED?

BECAUSE IT'S OLD.

WE HAVEN'T ANY USE FOR OLD THINGS HERE.

EVEN WHEN THEY'RE BEAUTIFUL?

PARTICULARLY WHEN THEY'RE BEAUTIFUL. BEAUTY'S ATTRACTIVE, AND WE DON'T WANT PEOPLE TO BE ATTRACTED BY OLD THINGS.

WE WANT THEM TO LIKE NEW ONES.

BUT THE NEW ONES ARE STUPID AND HORRIBLE. WHY DON'T YOU LET THEM SEE *OTHELLO* INSTEAD?

I'VE TOLD YOU; IT'S OLD.

BESIDES, THEY COULDN'T UNDERSTAND IT.

WELL, THAT'S TRUE.

WELL THEN, WHY NOT SOMETHING THAT'S LIKE *OTHELLO*, AND THAT THEY COULD UNDERSTAND?

BECAUSE, IF IT WERE REALLY LIKE *OTHELLO* NOBODY COULD UNDERSTAND IT, HOWEVER NEW IT MIGHT BE. AND IF IT WERE NEW, IT COULDN'T POSSIBLY BE LIKE *OTHELLO*.

WHY NOT?

YES, WHY NOT?

BECAUSE OUR WORLD IS NOT THE SAME AS OTHELLO'S WORLD.

YOU CAN'T MAKE FLIVVERS WITHOUT STEEL--AND YOU CAN'T MAKE TRAGEDIES WITHOUT SOCIAL INSTABILITY.

THE WORLD'S STABLE NOW. PEOPLE ARE HAPPY; THEY GET WHAT THEY WANT, AND THEY NEVER WANT WHAT THEY CAN'T GET. THEY'RE WELL-OFF; THEY'RE SAFE; THEY'RE NEVER ILL; THEY'RE NOT AFRAID OF DEATH . . .

THEY'RE BLISSFULLY IGNORANT OF PASSION AND OLD AGE; THEY'RE PLAGUED WITH NO MOTHERS OR FATHERS; THEY'VE GOT NO SPOUSES, OR CHILDREN, OR LOVERS TO FEEL STRONGLY ABOUT.

THEY'RE SO CONDITIONED THAT THEY PRACTICALLY CAN'T HELP BEHAVING AS THEY OUGHT TO BEHAVE.

AND IF ANYTHING SHOULD GO WRONG, THERE'S SOMA.

WHICH YOU GO AND CHUCK OUT THE WINDOW IN THE NAME OF LIBERTY, MR. SAVAGE.

LIBERTY!

EXPECTING DELTAS TO KNOW WHAT LIBERTY IS! AND NOW EXPECTING THEM TO UNDERSTAND *OTHELLO*!

ALL THE SAME, *OTHELLO*'S GOOD.

OF COURSE IT IS. THAT'S THE PRICE WE HAVE TO PAY FOR STABILITY. YOU'VE GOT TO CHOOSE BETWEEN HAPPINESS AND WHAT PEOPLE USED TO CALL HIGH ART. WE'VE SACRIFICED THE HIGH ART.

WE HAVE THE FEELIES AND THE SCENT ORGAN INSTEAD.

BUT THEY DON'T MEAN ANYTHING.

THEY MEAN THEMSELVES. THEY MEAN A LOT OF AGREEABLE SENSATIONS TO THE AUDIENCE.

BUT THEY'RE . . . THEY'RE TOLD BY AN IDIOT.

HA HA! YOU'RE NOT BEING VERY POLITE TO YOUR FRIEND, MR. WATSON. ONE OF OUR MOST DISTINGUISHED EMOTIONAL ENGINEERS . . .

BUT HE'S RIGHT. BECAUSE IT IS IDIOTIC.

WRITING WHEN THERE'S NOTHING TO SAY . . .

BUT THAT'S WHAT REQUIRES THE MOST ENORMOUS INGENUITY. YOU'RE MAKING FLIVVERS OUT OF THE ABSOLUTE MINIMUM OF STEEL--WORKS OF ART OUT OF PRACTICALLY NOTHING BUT PURE SENSATION.

IT ALL LOOKS PRETTY HORRIBLE TO ME.

OF COURSE IT DOES. ACTUAL HAPPINESS ALWAYS LOOKS PRETTY SQUALID IN COMPARISON WITH THE OVERCOMPENSATIONS FOR MISERY. STABILITY ISN'T NEARLY SO SPECTACULAR AS INSTABILITY.

AND BEING CONTENTED HAS NONE OF THE GLAMOR OF A GOOD FIGHT AGAINST MISFORTUNE, NONE OF THE PICTURESQUENESS OF A STRUGGLE WITH TEMPTATION, OR A FATAL OVERTHROW BY PASSION OR DOUBT.

HAPPINESS IS NEVER GRAND.

I SUPPOSE NOT. BUT NEED IT BE QUITE SO BAD AS THOSE TWINS?

OUR BOKANOVSKY GROUPS ARE THE GYROSCOPE THAT STABILIZES THE ROCKET OF STATE ON ITS UNSWERVING COURSE.

WHY HAVE THEM AT ALL? WHY DON'T YOU MAKE EVERYONE AN ALPHA-DOUBLE-PLUS?

BECAUSE WE DON'T WANT TO HAVE OUR THROATS CUT.

WE BELIEVE IN HAPPINESS AND STABILITY. A SOCIETY OF ALPHAS COULDN'T FAIL TO BE UNSTABLE AND MISERABLE. THE CYPRUS EXPERIMENT WAS CONVINCING.

WHAT WAS THAT?

AN EXPERIMENT IN REBOTTLING.

IN A.F. 473 THE ISLAND OF CYPRUS WAS CLEARED OF ITS INHABITANTS AND RE-COLONIZED WITH A SPECIALLY PREPARED BATCH OF TWENTY-TWO THOUSAND ALPHAS. THE RESULT EXACTLY FULFILLED THEORETICAL EXPECTATIONS.

THE LAND WASN'T PROPERLY WORKED; THERE WERE STRIKES IN ALL THE FACTORIES; THE LAWS WERE SET AT NAUGHT, ORDERS DISOBEYED. WITHIN SIX YEARS THEY WERE HAVING A FIRST-CLASS CIVIL WAR.

THE OPTIMUM POPULATION IS MODELLED ON THE ICEBERG--EIGHT NINTHS BELOW THE WATERLINE, ONE NINTH ABOVE.

AND THEY'RE HAPPY BELOW THE WATERLINE?

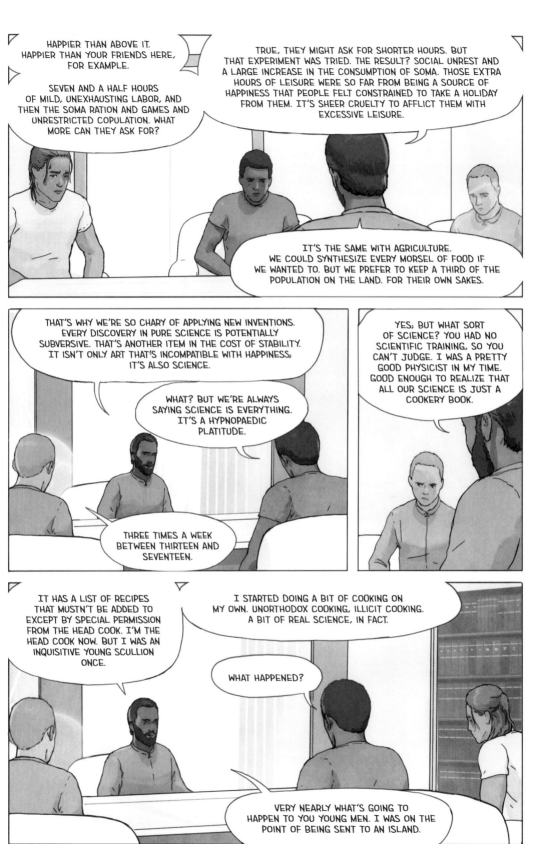

HAPPIER THAN ABOVE IT. HAPPIER THAN YOUR FRIENDS HERE, FOR EXAMPLE.

SEVEN AND A HALF HOURS OF MILD, UNEXHAUSTING LABOR, AND THEN THE SOMA RATION AND GAMES AND UNRESTRICTED COPULATION. WHAT MORE CAN THEY ASK FOR?

TRUE, THEY MIGHT ASK FOR SHORTER HOURS. BUT THAT EXPERIMENT WAS TRIED. THE RESULT? SOCIAL UNREST AND A LARGE INCREASE IN THE CONSUMPTION OF SOMA. THOSE EXTRA HOURS OF LEISURE WERE SO FAR FROM BEING A SOURCE OF HAPPINESS THAT PEOPLE FELT CONSTRAINED TO TAKE A HOLIDAY FROM THEM. IT'S SHEER CRUELTY TO AFFLICT THEM WITH EXCESSIVE LEISURE.

IT'S THE SAME WITH AGRICULTURE. WE COULD SYNTHESIZE EVERY MORSEL OF FOOD IF WE WANTED TO. BUT WE PREFER TO KEEP A THIRD OF THE POPULATION ON THE LAND. FOR THEIR OWN SAKES.

THAT'S WHY WE'RE SO CHARY OF APPLYING NEW INVENTIONS. EVERY DISCOVERY IN PURE SCIENCE IS POTENTIALLY SUBVERSIVE. THAT'S ANOTHER ITEM IN THE COST OF STABILITY. IT ISN'T ONLY ART THAT'S INCOMPATIBLE WITH HAPPINESS; IT'S ALSO SCIENCE.

WHAT? BUT WE'RE ALWAYS SAYING SCIENCE IS EVERYTHING. IT'S A HYPNOPAEDIC PLATITUDE.

THREE TIMES A WEEK BETWEEN THIRTEEN AND SEVENTEEN.

YES, BUT WHAT SORT OF SCIENCE? YOU HAD NO SCIENTIFIC TRAINING, SO YOU CAN'T JUDGE. I WAS A PRETTY GOOD PHYSICIST IN MY TIME. GOOD ENOUGH TO REALIZE THAT ALL OUR SCIENCE IS JUST A COOKERY BOOK.

IT HAS A LIST OF RECIPES THAT MUSTN'T BE ADDED TO EXCEPT BY SPECIAL PERMISSION FROM THE HEAD COOK. I'M THE HEAD COOK NOW. BUT I WAS AN INQUISITIVE YOUNG SCULLION ONCE.

I STARTED DOING A BIT OF COOKING ON MY OWN. UNORTHODOX COOKING, ILLICIT COOKING. A BIT OF REAL SCIENCE, IN FACT.

WHAT HAPPENED?

VERY NEARLY WHAT'S GOING TO HAPPEN TO YOU YOUNG MEN. I WAS ON THE POINT OF BEING SENT TO AN ISLAND.

SEND **ME** TO AN ISLAND?

YOU CAN'T SEND *ME*. I HAVEN'T DONE ANYTHING.

IT WAS THE OTHERS. I SWEAR IT WAS THE OTHERS.

OH, PLEASE DON'T SEND ME TO ICELAND. I PROMISE I'LL DO WHAT I OUGHT TO DO.

GIVE ME ANOTHER CHANCE. PLEASE GIVE ME ANOTHER CHANCE.

BOOP

SEND THREE MEN.

YOUR FORDSHIP, PLEASE . . .

TAKE MR. MARX INTO A BEDROOM.

NOT TO ICELAND! OH, PLEASE, YOUR FORDSHIP, PLEASE . . .

GIVE HIM A GOOD SOMA VAPORIZATION.

NOT TO ICELAND!

ONE WOULD THINK HE WAS GOING TO HAVE HIS THROAT CUT.

HE'S BEING SENT TO AN ISLAND. A PLACE WHERE HE'LL MEET THE MOST INTERESTING SET OF MEN AND WOMEN TO BE FOUND ANYWHERE IN THE WORLD. ALL THE PEOPLE WHO AREN'T SATISFIED WITH ORTHODOXY, WHO'VE GOT INDEPENDENT IDEAS OF THEIR OWN.

I ALMOST ENVY YOU, MR. WATSON.

THEN WHY AREN'T YOU ON AN ISLAND YOURSELF?

BECAUSE, FINALLY, I PREFERRED THIS. I CHOSE THIS AND LET THE SCIENCE GO.

I'M INTERESTED IN TRUTH, I LIKE SCIENCE. BUT TRUTH'S A MENACE, SCIENCE IS A PUBLIC DANGER. AS DANGEROUS AS IT'S BEEN BENEFICENT. IT HAS GIVEN US THE STABLEST EQUILIBRIUM IN HISTORY, BUT WE CAN'T ALLOW IT TO UNDO ITS OWN GOOD WORK.

WE DON'T ALLOW IT TO DEAL WITH ANY BUT THE MOST IMMEDIATE PROBLEMS OF THE MOMENT.

IT'S CURIOUS TO READ WHAT PEOPLE IN THE TIME OF OUR FORD USED TO WRITE ABOUT SCIENTIFIC PROGRESS.

THEY SEEMED TO HAVE IMAGINED THAT IT COULD BE ALLOWED TO GO ON INDEFINITELY, REGARDLESS OF EVERYTHING ELSE. KNOWLEDGE WAS THE HIGHEST GOOD, TRUTH THE SUPREME VALUE.

OUR FORD HIMSELF DID A GREAT DEAL TO SHIFT THE EMPHASIS FROM TRUTH AND BEAUTY TO COMFORT AND HAPPINESS. MASS PRODUCTION DEMANDED THE SHIFT.

BUT IT WAS AFTER THE NINE YEARS' WAR THAT SCIENCE FIRST BEGAN TO BE CONTROLLED. WHAT'S THE POINT OF TRUTH OR BEAUTY OR KNOWLEDGE WHEN ANTHRAX BOMBS ARE POPPING ALL AROUND YOU?

PEOPLE WERE READY TO HAVE EVEN THEIR APPETITES CONTROLLED AFTER THAT. ANYTHING FOR A QUIET LIFE.

WE'VE GONE ON CONTROLLING EVER SINCE.

ONE CAN'T HAVE SOMETHING FOR NOTHING. HAPPINESS HAS GOT TO BE PAID FOR. YOU'RE PAYING FOR IT, MR. WATSON, BECAUSE YOU HAPPEN TO BE TOO MUCH INTERESTED IN BEAUTY. I WAS TOO MUCH INTERESTED IN TRUTH; I PAID TOO.

BUT YOU DIDN'T GO TO AN ISLAND.

THAT'S HOW I PAID: BY CHOOSING TO SERVE HAPPINESS. OTHER PEOPLE'S-- NOT MINE.

IT'S A GOOD THING THERE ARE SO MANY ISLANDS IN THE WORLD. I DON'T KNOW WHAT WE'D DO WITHOUT THEM. PUT YOU ALL IN THE LETHAL CHAMBER, I SUPPOSE!

BY THE WAY, MR. WATSON, WOULD YOU LIKE A TROPICAL CLIMATE? OR SOMETHING MORE BRACING?

I SHOULD LIKE A THOROUGHLY BAD CLIMATE. I BELIEVE ONE WOULD WRITE BETTER IF THE CLIMATE WERE BAD.

IF THERE WERE A LOT OF WIND AND STORMS, FOR EXAMPLE.

I LIKE YOUR SPIRIT, MR. WATSON. I LIKE IT VERY MUCH INDEED. AS MUCH AS I OFFICIALLY DISAPPROVE OF IT.

HOW ABOUT THE FALKLAND ISLANDS?

YES, I THINK THAT WILL DO.

AND NOW, IF YOU DON'T MIND, I'LL GO AND SEE HOW POOR BERNARD'S GETTING ON.

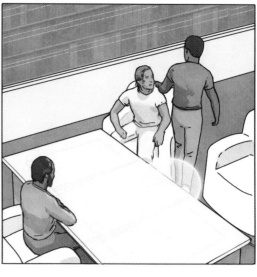

ART, SCIENCE--YOU SEEM TO HAVE PAID A FAIRLY HIGH PRICE FOR YOUR HAPPINESS. ANYTHING ELSE?

WELL, RELIGION, OF COURSE.

THERE USED TO BE SOMETHING CALLED GOD--BEFORE THE NINE YEARS' WAR.

BOOP

IT'S A SUBJECT THAT HAS ALWAYS HAD A GREAT INTEREST FOR ME.

I'VE GOT PLENTY MORE. A WHOLE COLLECTION OF PORNOGRAPHIC BOOKS.

The Imitation of Christ

The Holy Bible

GOD IN THE SAFE, FORD ON THE SHELVES.

IF YOU KNOW ABOUT GOD, WHY DON'T YOU TELL THEM? WHY DON'T YOU GIVE THEM THESE BOOKS ABOUT GOD?

FOR THE SAME REASON WE DON'T GIVE THEM *OTHELLO*: THEY'RE OLD. THEY'RE ABOUT GOD HUNDREDS OF YEARS AGO, NOT ABOUT GOD NOW.

BUT GOD DOESN'T CHANGE.

MEN DO, THOUGH.

ONE OF THE NUMEROUS THINGS IN HEAVEN AND EARTH THAT THE PHILOSOPHERS DIDN'T DREAM ABOUT WAS *THIS*.

US, THE MODERN WORLD.

"YOU CAN ONLY BE INDEPENDENT OF GOD WHILE YOU'VE GOT YOUTH AND PROSPERITY; INDEPENDENCE WON'T TAKE YOU RIGHT UP TO THE END." WELL, WE'VE NOW GOT YOUTH AND PROSPERITY RIGHT UP TO THE END.

"THE RELIGIOUS SENTIMENT WILL COMPENSATE US FOR ALL OUR LOSSES." BUT THERE AREN'T ANY LOSSES FOR US TO COMPENSATE.

AND WHY SHOULD WE GO HUNTING FOR A SUBSTITUTE FOR YOUTHFUL DESIRES, WHEN YOUTHFUL DESIRES NEVER FAIL?

WHY SEEK A SUBSTITUTE FOR DISTRACTIONS, WHEN WE GO ON ENJOYING ALL THE OLD FOOLERIES TO THE VERY LAST?

WHAT NEED HAVE WE OF REPOSE WHEN OUR MINDS AND BODIES CONTINUE TO DELIGHT IN ACTIVITY? OF CONSOLATION WHEN WE HAVE SOMA? OF SOMETHING IMMOVABLE WHEN THERE IS THE SOCIAL ORDER?

THEN YOU THINK THERE IS NO GOD?

NO, I THINK THERE QUITE PROBABLY IS ONE. BUT HE MANIFESTS HIMSELF IN DIFFERENT WAYS TO DIFFERENT PEOPLES.

IN PRE-MODERN TIMES HE MANIFESTS HIMSELF AS THE BEING THAT'S DESCRIBED IN THESE BOOKS.

HOW DOES HE MANIFEST HIMSELF NOW?

NOW HE MANIFESTS HIMSELF AS AN ABSENCE; AS THOUGH HE WEREN'T HERE AT ALL.

THAT'S YOUR FAULT.

CALL IT THE FAULT OF CIVILIZATION. GOD ISN'T COMPATIBLE WITH MACHINERY AND SCIENTIFIC MEDICINE AND UNIVERSAL HAPPINESS.

YOU MUST MAKE YOUR CHOICE. OUR CIVILIZATION HAS CHOSEN MACHINERY AND MEDICINE AND HAPPINESS.

THAT'S WHY I HAVE TO KEEP THESE BOOKS LOCKED UP IN THE SAFE. THEY'RE SMUT. PEOPLE WOULD BE SHOCKED IF . . .

BUT ISN'T IT *NATURAL* TO FEEL THERE'S A GOD?

YOU MIGHT AS WELL ASK IF IT'S NATURAL TO DO UP ONE'S TROUSERS WITH ZIPPERS.

PEOPLE BELIEVE IN GOD BECAUSE THEY'VE BEEN CONDITIONED TO BELIEVE IN GOD.

BUT ALL THE SAME, IT IS NATURAL TO BELIEVE IN GOD WHEN YOU'RE ALONE--QUITE ALONE, IN THE NIGHT, THINKING ABOUT DEATH.

BUT PEOPLE ARE NEVER ALONE NOW. WE MAKE THEM HATE SOLITUDE; AND WE ARRANGE THEIR LIVES SO THAT IT'S ALMOST IMPOSSIBLE FOR THEM TO EVER HAVE IT.

AT MALPAIS I SUFFERED BECAUSE I WAS SHUT OUT OF COMMUNAL ACTIVITIES.

HERE I SUFFER BECAUSE I CANNOT ESCAPE THEM.

DO YOU REMEMBER THAT BIT IN *KING LEAR*? "THE GODS ARE JUST, AND OF OUR PLEASANT VICES MAKE INSTRUMENTS TO PLAGUE US; THE DARK AND VICIOUS PLACE WHERE THEE HE GOT COST HIM HIS EYES."

AND EDMUND ANSWERS-- YOU REMEMBER, HE'S WOUNDED, HE'S DYING--"THOU HAST SPOKEN RIGHT; 'TIS TRUE. THE WHEEL IS COME FULL CIRCLE; I AM HERE."

WELL, WHAT ABOUT THAT, NOW? DOESN'T THERE SEEM TO BE A GOD MANAGING THINGS, PUNISHING, REWARDING?

WELL, DOES THERE? YOU CAN INDULGE IN ANY NUMBER OF PLEASANT VICES WITH A FREEMARTIN AND RUN NO RISK OF HAVING YOUR EYES PUT OUT BY YOUR SON'S MISTRESS.

"THE WHEEL IS COME FULL CIRCLE; I AM HERE." BUT WHERE WOULD EDMUND BE NOWADAYS?

SITTING IN A PNEUMATIC CHAIR, WITH HIS ARM ROUND A GIRL'S WAIST, SUCKING AWAY AT HIS SEX-HORMONE CHEWING GUM AND LOOKING AT THE FEELIES.

THE GODS ARE JUST. NO DOUBT.

BUT THEIR CODE OF LAW IS DICTATED, IN THE LAST RESORT, BY THE PEOPLE WHO ORGANIZE SOCIETY. PROVIDENCE TAKES ITS CUE FROM MEN.

ARE YOU QUITE SURE THAT THE EDMUND IN THAT PNEUMATIC CHAIR HASN'T BEEN JUST AS HEAVILY PUNISHED AS THE EDMUND WHO'S BLEEDING TO DEATH?

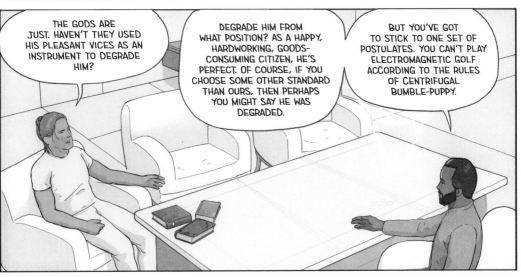

THE GODS ARE JUST. HAVEN'T THEY USED HIS PLEASANT VICES AS AN INSTRUMENT TO DEGRADE HIM?

DEGRADE HIM FROM WHAT POSITION? AS A HAPPY, HARDWORKING, GOODS-CONSUMING CITIZEN, HE'S PERFECT. OF COURSE, IF YOU CHOOSE SOME OTHER STANDARD THAN OURS, THEN PERHAPS YOU MIGHT SAY HE WAS DEGRADED.

BUT YOU'VE GOT TO STICK TO ONE SET OF POSTULATES. YOU CAN'T PLAY ELECTROMAGNETIC GOLF ACCORDING TO THE RULES OF CENTRIFUGAL BUMBLE-PUPPY.

IF YOU ALLOWED YOURSELVES TO THINK OF GOD, YOU WOULDN'T ALLOW YOURSELVES TO BE DEGRADED BY PLEASANT VICES.

YOU'D HAVE A REASON FOR BEARING THINGS PATIENTLY, FOR DOING THINGS WITH COURAGE. YOU'D HAVE A REASON FOR SELF-DENIAL.

YOU'D HAVE A REASON FOR CHASTITY.

BUT CHASTITY MEANS PASSION. AND PASSION MEANS INSTABILITY. AND INSTABILITY MEANS THE END OF CIVILIZATION.

NOBILITY AND HEROISM ARE SYMPTOMS OF POLITICAL INEFFICIENCY.

IN A PROPERLY ORGANIZED SOCIETY, NOBODY HAS ANY OPPORTUNITIES FOR BEING NOBLE OR HEROIC. THERE AREN'T ANY WARS NOWADAYS. THE GREATEST CARE IS TAKEN TO PREVENT YOU FROM LOVING ANYONE TOO MUCH. THERE'S NO SUCH THING AS A DIVIDED ALLEGIANCE. NO TEMPTATIONS TO RESIST. AND IF EVER, BY SOME UNLUCKY CHANCE, ANYTHING UNPLEASANT SHOULD SOMEHOW HAPPEN, WHY, THERE'S ALWAYS SOMA.

IN THE PAST IT TOOK YEARS OF HARD MORAL TRAINING TO ACCOMPLISH RECONCILIATION WITH ONE'S ENEMIES, TO ACCOMPLISH PATIENCE.

NOW, YOU SWALLOW TWO OR THREE HALF-GRAM TABLETS AND THERE YOU ARE. ANYBODY CAN BE VIRTUOUS NOW. YOU CAN CARRY AT LEAST HALF YOUR MORALITY AROUND IN A BOTTLE.

CHRISTIANITY WITHOUT TEARS-- THAT'S WHAT SOMA IS.

BUT THE TEARS ARE NECESSARY.

THERE'S A STORY ONE OF THE OLD INDIANS USED TO TELL US, ABOUT THE GIRL OF MÁTSAKI.

THE YOUNG MEN WHO WANTED TO MARRY HER HAD TO DO A MORNING'S HOEING IN HER GARDEN. IT SEEMED EASY; BUT THERE WERE FLIES AND MOSQUITOES, MAGIC ONES. MOST OF THE YOUNG MEN SIMPLY COULDN'T STAND THE BITING AND STINGING.

BUT THE ONE THAT COULD--HE GOT THE GIRL.

CHARMING! BUT IN CIVILIZED COUNTRIES, YOU CAN HAVE GIRLS WITHOUT HOEING FOR THEM; AND THERE AREN'T ANY FLIES OR MOSQUITOES TO STING YOU. WE GOT RID OF THEM ALL.

YES, THAT'S JUST LIKE YOU. GET RID OF ANYTHING UNPLEASANT INSTEAD OF LEARNING TO PUT UP WITH IT.

YOU NEITHER SUFFER NOR OPPOSE. YOU JUST ABOLISH THE SLINGS AND ARROWS.

WHAT YOU NEED IS SOMETHING WITH TEARS FOR A CHANGE. NOTHING COSTS ENOUGH HERE.

EXPOSING WHAT IS MORTAL AND UNSURE TO ALL THAT FORTUNE, DEATH AND DANGER DARE, EVEN FOR AN EGGSHELL. ISN'T THERE SOMETHING IN THAT? ISN'T THERE SOMETHING IN LIVING DANGEROUSLY?

THERE'S A GREAT DEAL TO IT. MEN AND WOMEN MUST HAVE THEIR ADRENALS STIMULATED FROM TIME TO TIME.

THAT'S WHY WE'VE MADE THE VPS TREATMENTS COMPULSORY.

VPS?

VIOLENT PASSION SURROGATE. REGULARLY ONCE A MONTH. THE COMPLETE PHYSIOLOGICAL EQUIVALENT OF FEAR AND RAGE.

ALL THE TONIC EFFECTS OF MURDERING DESDEMONA AND BEING MURDERED BY OTHELLO, WITHOUT ANY OF THE INCONVENIENCES.

BUT I LIKE THE INCONVENIENCES.

WE DON'T. WE PREFER TO DO THINGS COMFORTABLY.

I DON'T WANT COMFORT. I WANT GOD, I WANT POETRY, I WANT REAL DANGER, I WANT FREEDOM, I WANT GOODNESS.

I WANT SIN.

IN FACT, YOU'RE CLAIMING THE RIGHT TO BE UNHAPPY.

NOT TO MENTION THE RIGHT TO GROW OLD AND UGLY AND IMPOTENT; THE RIGHT TO HAVE SYPHILIS AND CANCER; THE RIGHT TO HAVE TOO LITTLE TO EAT; THE RIGHT TO LIVE IN CONSTANT APPREHENSION OF WHAT MAY HAPPEN TOMORROW; THE RIGHT TO BE TORTURED BY UNSPEAKABLE PAINS OF EVERY KIND.

I CLAIM
THEM ALL.

YOU'RE
WELCOME.

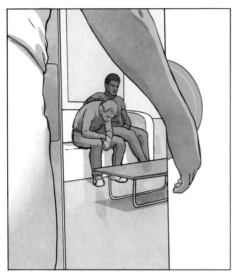

JOHN!

IS ANYTHING THE MATTER?

I SAY, YOU DO LOOK ILL, JOHN.

DID YOU EAT SOMETHING THAT DIDN'T AGREE WITH YOU?

I ATE CIVILIZATION.

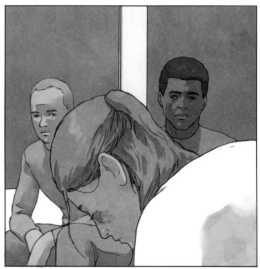

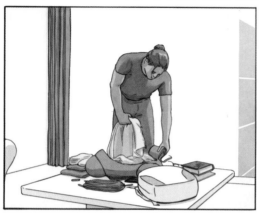

EVERYBODY'S HAPPY

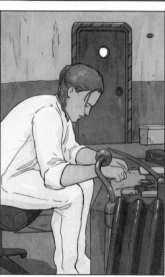

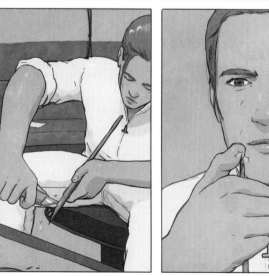

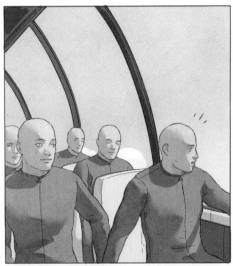

TCHAK

TCHAK

TCHAK

SHINK

WHAT DO YOU WANT WITH ME?

DO THE WHIPPING STUNT.

YES, LET'S SEE THE WHIPPING STUNT!

WE--WANT-- THE WHIP.

WE--WANT-- THE WHIP.

WE--WANT-- THE WHIP.

WE--WANT-- THE WHIP.

WE--WANT-- THE WHIP.

WE--WANT--

RAAARGHHH

AAAARGHH

TCHAK

STRUMPET!

FITCHEW!

HENRY, HENRY, HELP M--

TCHAK

THACK

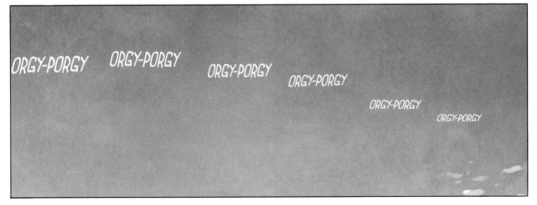

OH, MY
GOD, MY
GOD.

MR. SAVAGE?

MR. SAVAGE?

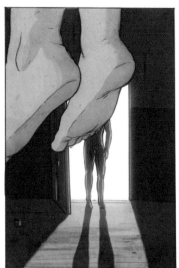

MR. SAVAGE!